Developing
SPANISH

PHOTOCOPIABLE LANGUAGE ACTIVITIES
FOR BEGINNERS

Libro Tres

**Anna Grassi and
Cristina Kollinger Collesei**

A & C BLACK

For Rupali, Tommaso, Fleck and Selva

Published 2007 by A & C Black Publishers Limited
38 Soho Square, London W1D 3HB
www.acblack.com

ISBN: 978-0-7136-7931-1

Editor: Jane Klima
Design: Susan McIntyre

The authors and publishers would like to thank Lindsay Blundell and
Sarah Potter for their assistance in producing this book.

Printed in Great Britain by Caligraving Ltd, Thetford, Norfolk.

This book is produced using paper that is made from wood grown in
managed, sustainable forests. It is natural, renewable and recyclable.
The logging and manufacturing processes conform to the environmental
regulations of the country of origin.

Contents

Introduction

Developing Spanish is a series of three photocopiable activity books which support the teaching of Spanish at primary level. Each book provides a range of activities which aim to develop the children's ability to understand and respond in Spanish. The series has been designed in line with the Key Stage 2 *Framework for languages* of the National Languages Strategy and offers opportunities to develop and extend the main learning objectives, including:

Oracy
- Identifying key words and phrases in short passages of spoken Spanish;
- Asking and answering questions on a range of topics;
- Engaging in simple conversations and beginning to use language imaginatively.

Literacy
- Reading a variety of short texts;
- Creating simple texts for different purposes;
- Learning about the basic writing system, the spelling and the structure of Spanish.

Intercultural understanding
- Learning about aspects of Spanish culture and traditions through comparisons with their own culture;
- Recognising similarities and differences between people.

Knowledge about language (KAL)
- Reflecting on linguistic similarities and differences such as sounds, the written word, phrasing and sentence order between Spanish and English.

Language learning strategies (LLS)
- Providing teachers with examples of learning strategies to help children to learn and to retain Spanish.

Teaching requirements

The teaching suggestions and learning activities in **Developing Spanish** may be integrated into classroom lessons or used during after-school clubs or by parents at home. Ideally, all teaching should be in Spanish, but this is not essential – the books are written so that they can be used by a non-native speaker if necessary. Translations are provided for all key vocabulary and each book includes a guide to Spanish pronunciation.

The activities require very few resources beyond pencils, crayons, scissors, card and other general classroom items. Any other materials you will need are specified in the **Notes on the activities** (for example, pictures from magazines, travel brochures, etc.).

Pronunciation

Spanish is a phonetic language – each letter or combination of letters once mastered is always pronounced the same. Most of the Spanish alphabet sounds the same as the English alphabet, but there are some notable exceptions and a few extra letters which have to be learned. You will find all the guidance you need to these and other basic sounds in Spanish in the pronunciation guide on page 8.

Developing Spanish focuses on Spanish as spoken in Spain. Pronunciation variations exist between Iberian Spanish and Latin American Spanish and even between some regions within Spain. For example, *cena* and *cine*, which start with a 'th' sound in most of Spain, are pronounced with an initial 's' sound in Latin America and in some Spanish regions such as Andalucía (Andalusia) and Canarias (the Canary Islands).

Many of the resources listed on page 62 feature guides to pronunciation and/or spoken-word audio tapes/CDs. An online spoken pronunciation guide is available on the publisher's companion website to this series at www.acblack.com/developingspanish.

Developing Spanish Libro Tres

This third book in the series presents ideas and activities intended to promote confidence and encourage more complex communication in Spanish. The topics offer the children practical opportunities in which to apply Spanish language structures. The activities are up-to-date and aim to reflect everyday life and aspects of culture in Spain.

The five topics are:

- date and time: days of the week, months, seasons, expressing time
- weather: describing the weather, items of clothing
- daily life: routine, timetables, expressing frequency
- technology and the environment: television, computers, recycling
- Spain and the world: points of the compass, countries, nationalities.

Topics

Each of the five topics includes:

- **key vocabulary, expressions and grammar** – these are listed along with their translation;
- **teaching ideas** to help you to make the most of the topic – these provide suggestions for games, songs, rhymes and role-plays, as well as notes on Spanish culture;
- **notes on the activities** for all the individual photocopiable sheets – these offer introductory or warm-up ideas, suggestions for follow-up work, and page-specific grammar notes where necessary;
- **photocopiable activity sheets**.

Additionally, Topics 2, 3 and 5 conclude with a double-page **picture dictionary**.

Photocopiable activity sheets

There are up to eight photocopiable activity sheets for each topic. Each sheet features:

- a relevant, active vocabulary title;
- instructions and text in simple, clear Spanish with easy-to-recognise activity icons;
- word banks to help the children to carry out the task where appropriate;
- appealing illustrations of typically Spanish objects, situations and scenes. The main characters are a Spanish boy and girl, Carlos and Marta, who appear throughout the series;

 Carlos  Marta

- a **Teachers' note** which includes:
  - translation of the page title and instructions, and, following a bullet point (•), of the extension task;
  - the learning objective;
  - a summary of the language skills and vocabulary the children will need to practise before using the sheet;
  - advice on how to use the activity sheet.

Most activity sheets end with a challenge (**Y ahora** – And now…), a writing or speaking activity which aims to reinforce language learned in the main activity and to help the children to become more confident and independent in its use. A notebook or separate sheet of paper will be required for the children to complete some of these extension activities, or they could use the back of the sheet.

Key to the activity icons

The Spanish verbs used in the instructions following the activity icons are in the imperative (command) form of the second person singular (the informal *tú*).

 Mira (Look)

 Lee (Read)

 Escribe (Write)

 Dibuja (Draw)

 Colorea (Colour)

 Habla (Speak)

 Escoge (Choose)

 Busca (Find)

 Corta (Cut)

 Pega (Glue)

 Une (Join)

 Ordena (Order)

 Cuenta (Count)

 Juega (Play)

Picture dictionaries

These three illustrated spreads feature a title and 22 vocabulary words. The border illustrations represent nouns if they are inside a circle, verbs if they are inside a square and adjectives if they are inside an octagon. This distinction can be used as a learning strategy to help the children to reflect on the structure of language.

la tienda   escalar   seco

The picture dictionaries can be used in a number of ways:

- To introduce and/or revise written and spoken vocabulary. Mask the words and give each child a copy. Ask the children to write the names or to say the words in Spanish.

- To revise grammar. Mask the articles and ask the children to write them in or to say them aloud. The children can also identify the gender of words by using different coloured highlighters or by underlining or circling words.

- For a variety of spoken games and activities such as counting, describing, guessing and finding. For example, ask the children ¿Qué tiempo hace en la montaña? (What's the weather like on the mountain?) or ¿Quién espera al niño? (Who is waiting for the boy?) or ¿Qué hace el señor? (What is the man doing?)

Additional suggestions for using the picture dictionaries are provided in the corresponding topic's teaching ideas.

Recommended resources

Recommended suppliers of Spanish books and teaching materials, suggested websites for teachers and for children, and details of curriculum information and teaching methods are listed on page 62.

Answers

Turn to pages 63 and 64 for answers to all the questions, wordsearches, puzzles and crosswords featured on the activity sheets.

Pull-out frieze

Inside the back cover is an appealing giant colour pull-out frieze to be displayed in the classroom. The frieze presents a Spanish scene with 20 key words, including verbs, dotted around the illustration. Words in rounded boxes are nouns; words in rectangular boxes are verbs.

You can use the frieze as a warm-up at the beginning of each lesson to revise vocabulary and as a short conversation starter. For example, ask individual children questions about the frieze such as ¿Qué tiempo hace en este dibujo? (What is the weather like in this picture?), then follow up with a supplementary question about themselves: ¿Qué tiempo te gusta más? ¿Por qué? (What kind of weather do you like best? Why?)

As with the picture dictionaries, the shape code may be used as a learning strategy. Go over the words on the frieze and discuss their function according to whether they are in a rounded box or in a rectangular box. Draw two different large shapes on the board, one for nouns and one for verbs. Ask the children to think of either a noun or a verb and to write it on a post-it note. They should then exchange their slips of paper, take turns to read them aloud and stick them in the correct shape on the board.

General teaching suggestions

One of the keys to success in learning a foreign language is constant practice. The activities contained in **Developing Spanish** offer plenty of opportunities for varied and differentiated practice.

Here are some extra suggestions on how to help the children to learn and to practise new vocabulary:

Drills and repetition are useful for pronunciation practice and to help the children to memorise words. For example, prompt the children to repeat words *lentamente* (slowly), *rápidamente* (quickly), *susurrando* (in a whisper), *fuerte* (loudly), etc.

Pairs of children could practise vocabulary by taking turns to count or find the opposites of adjectives or by playing word association games. The gender of nouns can be reinforced by one child saying the noun and his or her partner supplying the definite or indefinite article.

Oral games and **role-play activities** encourage the children to become more comfortable with the language. An example of a simple oral word game is *La maleta* (Suitcase) where the first child says *Voy a Madrid y llevo un gato* (I'm going to Madrid and I'm taking a cat). The second child repeats the sentence and adds a second word. The third child repeats the sentence and adds a third word and so on.

Playing *El ahorcado* (Hangman) is a quick way for the children to revise vocabulary and spelling.

Another popular game is *Veo, veo* (I spy). This is useful for practising different categories of vocabulary. For example:

    A: *Veo, veo.*
    B: *¿Qué ves?*
    A: *Veo una ciudad española que empieza con la 'B'.*
    B: *¿Bilbao?*
    A: *¡No!*
    B: *¿Barcelona?*
    A: *¡Sí!*

The oral game *¡Qué confusión!* (What a muddle!) can be adapted to fit a variety of scenarios: for example, days of the week, months of the year, the order in which things are done, etc. Feed the children a piece of false information or one incorrect word or phrase in a series of correct phrases. The first child to realise shouts *¡Qué confusión!* and has the chance to say the correct information instead.

The children will also enjoy miming action verbs and preparing simple sketches or role-plays. Use the dialogues presented in the activity sheets for ideas.

Card games such as Pelmanism (Pairs) and Snap! using flashcards are a fun way for children to consolidate vocabulary. Pelmanism can be played individually, in pairs, or even as a whole class with enlarged cards. When playing Snap!, the children must call out the Spanish word on the card instead of the word 'Snap!'

Another important element in learning a foreign language is a comfortable learning environment. Use Spanish as much as possible along with a variety of teaching styles. It is helpful to establish a routine at the beginning of every lesson so that the children know what to expect. Always exchange greetings in the same way at the start of each session. The beginning of a lesson is a good time to review previously introduced material through drills and questions.

Praise and encouragement in Spanish also help to foster a relaxed learning atmosphere. Some useful expressions are *¡Excelente!* (Excellent!), *¡Muy bien!* (Very good!), *¡Buen trabajo!* (Good work!), *¡Perfecto!* (Perfect!)

A stimulating learning environment can be attained by displaying the children's work, the **Developing Spanish** pull-out friezes, enlarged copies of the picture dictionaries, posters, a *¡Bienvenidos!* (Welcome!) sign, etc. Use real-life visual aids such as Spanish travel posters and brochures, postcards, banknotes, coins, menus, train tickets and product labels for the children to touch and see. Laminating visual aids will help to extend their life.

An effective way to boost the children's confidence in their oral abilities is to organise a 'show' of what they have learned for parents and/or schoolmates. They could perform short sketches that they have written themselves, or they could play an oral game in teams. For instance, you could divide the class into two teams lined up at one end of the room. At the other end set up a box full of colourful clothes and another box of slips of paper with the names and colours of the items of clothing written on them: for example, *Una bufanda naranja* (An orange scarf) or *Un sombrero verde* (A green hat). To play, the first child in each team runs to the box of slips, takes one, runs back and reads it aloud to the next child in his or her team. The second child runs to find the named item in the clothes box and puts it on over whatever he or she is already wearing. Once it is on properly, he or she picks another slip and runs back to tell the next person in line what to choose from the clothes box. The last person in the team has to tell the first person in line what to put on. The winners are the team who are first to be all wearing an item of clothing from the box.

Pronunciation guide

This page offers guidance on how to pronounce all the basic sounds of letters or combinations of letters in Spanish. Where possible, an English word containing the approximate sound is given for each one. Practise the sound by reading the practice words aloud several times.

You may want to ask a native Spanish speaker or a Spanish-language teacher to help you with the correct pronunciation, or you could use the online pronunciation guide which accompanies this series at www.acblack.com/developingspanish.

Note that both the guide below and the online guide reflect the pronunciation of Spanish as spoken in most of Spain. Pronunciation variations may be found in Latin American countries and in some regions of Spain.

a   like the 'a' sound in 'bad'
practice words: *la, casa, mamá*

e   like the 'e' sound in 'get'
practice words: *el, tres, tener*

i   like the 'ee' sound in 'feet', but shorter
practice words: *bici, mira, venir*

o   like the 'o' sound in 'box'
practice words: *no, moto, color*

u   like the 'oo' sound in 'tooth'
practice words: *una, usar, tu*

c   like the 'c' sound in 'cat' except before *e* or *i*
practice words: *café, comer, cubo*

   like the 'th' sound in 'thin' when before *e* or *i*
practice words: *cena, centro, cine*

ch like the 'ch' sound in 'church'
practice words: *mucho, ducha, coche*

g   like the 'g' sound in 'go' except before *e* or *i*
practice words: *gato, goma, regalo*

   like the 'ch' sound in 'loch' when before *e* or *i*
practice words: *gente, gimnasio*

gu like the 'g' sound in 'go' when before *e* or *i* (the *u* is silent)
practice words: *guerra, guitarra*

h   is always silent
practice words: *hacer, hermano*

j   like the 'ch' sound in 'loch'
practice words: *jamón, jugar, jugo*

ll depending on the region, like the 'lli' sound in 'million' or like the 'y' sound in 'yes'
practice words: *calle, silla, llama*

ñ   like the 'ni' sound in 'onion'
practice words: *niño, baño, mañana*

q   like the 'k' sound in 'kite' (it is always followed by a silent *u*)
practice words: *que, querer, quince*

r   a softly trilled 'r' sound like a Scottish *r*
practice words: *hora, mira*

   a strongly trilled 'r' sound when it's the first letter of a word
practice words: *rana, ropa*

rr a strongly trilled 'r' sound
practice words: *corre, aburrido*

v   like the 'b' sound in 'boy'
practice words: *ver, vivir*

y   like the 'y' sound in 'yes'
practice words: *yo, yogur*

z   like the 'th' sound in 'think'
practice words: *zapato, zorro, luz*

Topic 1: El calendario

Key vocabulary

el calendario	calendar
la hora	hour/time
el minuto	minute
el segundo	second
el día	day
la fecha	date
ayer	yesterday
hoy	today
mañana	tomorrow
la semana	week
lunes	Monday
martes	Tuesday
miércoles	Wednesday
jueves	Thursday
viernes	Friday
sábado	Saturday
domingo	Sunday
los meses	months
enero	January
febrero	February
marzo	March
abril	April
mayo	May
junio	June
julio	July
agosto	August
septiembre	September
octubre	October
noviembre	November
diciembre	December
las estaciones	seasons
la primavera	spring
el verano	summer
el otoño	autumn
el invierno	winter
el año	year

Expressions

¿Qué día es hoy?	What day is it today?
Hoy es...	Today is...
el lunes	on Monday
los domingos	on Sundays
¿Qué fecha es hoy?	What's the date today?
¿Qué hora es?	What time is it?

Teaching ideas

Vocabulary note
Once the children can tell the time in Spanish, practise the phrases *de la mañana* (in the morning), *de la tarde* (in the afternoon) and *de la noche* (in the evening/night) to specify the time of day: for example, *Son las ocho de la mañana/de la noche*. *Son las doce en punto* can also be expressed as *Es mediodía* (noon) or *Es medianoche* (midnight).

Classroom routine
Create a monthly calendar in Spanish with large squares for each day to display in class. On the calendar write the children's birthdays, holidays and any important school or class events. In Spain, Monday is regarded as the first day of the week. As part of your daily routine ask the children *¿Qué día es hoy?*, *¿Qué fecha es hoy?* or *¿Cuál es la fecha?* and write it at the top of the board. Encourage them to write the date in Spanish on their work.

Spanish culture
Spaniards celebrate many festivals (*fiestas*) throughout the year. Discuss the different types with the children and how they are celebrated. Here are just a few of the important *fiesta* dates – there are hundreds of others! (For interesting background material, see http://www.nickinman.com/fiestas.htm.)

Reyes Magos (Epiphany, 6 January) celebrates the Three Kings' visit to the baby Jesus. On this holiday Spanish children receive presents just as Jesus did. Processions of floats, bands and dancers take place throughout Spain.

Carnaval (Carnival, February) is celebrated all over Spain but the most important carnival is held in Las Palmas de Gran Canaria. People dress up in colourful costumes and dance through the streets in the *Gran cabalgata* (Grand cavalcade).

Semana Santa (Holy Week, March/April) is a very big event in Spain. Elaborate Easter processions depicting the Passion of Christ take place in many cities.

Feria de Abril (April Fair) is held in Seville shortly after Easter. Originally a cattle-trading fair, it is now a great *fiesta* with performances by *cantaores* (flamenco singers) and *bailaoras* (dancers) dressed in traditional Andalusian costumes, as well as parades, with decorated carriages and horses, and bullfights.

Sanfermines (Pamplona Bull Run, early July) attracts participants from all over the world. The streets of Pamplona are closed every morning and become a track for bulls to run after young men dressed in white with a red scarf tied round their neck or waist. The run ends at the bullring where, in the afternoon, a bullfight is held.

Día de la Hispanidad (12 October) commemorates Spain's national heritage and that of all nations with a Hispanic language, culture and history.

Día de la Constitución (Constitution Day, 6 December) celebrates the birth of Spain as a parliamentary monarchy.

Navidad (Christmas, 25 December) celebrates the birth of Christ. Live nativity scenes called *pesebres* are set up and acted out by townspeople all over Spain.

Notes on the activities

Page 11 Los días de la semana With the help of a calendar, or by writing the full date on the board, introduce the names of the days of the week. Prompt the children to repeat the days in order until they are familiar with them. Ask a different child *¿Qué día es hoy?* every day. Play *¡Qué confusión!* Ask in a doubtful way *¿Hoy es lunes?* The children should reply *¡No, es martes!* Change the day in the question and prompt the children to reply with the following day. As a variation change *hoy* to *mañana* in the question: *¿Mañana es domingo?* If the children are familiar with the past tense of *ser* (to be), ask *¿Ayer fue martes?* to talk about yesterday.

Page 12 Los meses del año With the aid of the pull-out frieze, introduce the months and seasons. Establish which months fall in which season: *¿Cuáles son los meses de la primavera?* Practise the names of the months by encouraging the children to say them in sequences of three. Ask which month comes before (*antes de*) or after (*después de*) the one you name. Follow up with questions such as *¿Cuáles meses tienen treinta días?* (Which months have 30 days?) Check the children are paying attention by asking *¿Cuál mes tiene veintinueve días?* (Which month has 29 days?) 'Leap year' is *año bisiesto*.

Page 13 ¿Qué fecha es hoy? Write some dates on the board as numbers. Point to each one and ask *¿Qué fecha es?* Help the children to work out the answer using their knowledge of numbers to 31 and the names of the months. Write the answers in words on the board. Point out that, unlike in English, there is only one way to formulate the date in Spanish: for example, *el 24 de enero*. All dates except the first day of the month are expressed using cardinal not ordinal numbers.

Page 14 ¡Feliz cumpleaños! Draw a birthday cake on the board and say *Mi cumpleaños es el … de …* Ask a child *¿Cuándo es tu cumpleaños?* As the children say their birthdays, write the date on the board in number form as a check. Ask those children who tackle the

extension activity to quiz several classmates about their birthdays, write down the information and then report back to the class: for example, *El cumpleaños de Mark es el tres de abril.* Sing *Cumpleaños Feliz* whenever someone celebrates a birthday (see **Developing Spanish Libro Uno**, page 28).

Page 15 Una fiesta española Show the children postcards, photographs or travel brochures depicting Spanish tourist sites and, if possible, traditional festivals. Prompt them to describe what they see in the images. Explain briefly about the *Sanfermines* festival in Pamplona. As a follow-up activity, look at a postcard in detail to revise the words *la postal* (postcard), *el sello* (stamp), *la dirección* (address). Ask the children to locate Pamplona and Córdoba on a map of Spain. If they are ready, invite them to write a postcard to Carlos or Marta briefly describing a local festival.

Page 16 La hora Start by revising numbers up to 60. On a large clock face show 12 o'clock and ask *¿Qué hora es?* Suggest the answer is *Es la una.* When the children correct you, show one o'clock and repeat *Es la una.* Work your way around the clock and practise saying the times at five-minute intervals. Point out that all times involving *la una* take the third person singular of the verb *ser* (*es*), while all times from two to 12 take the third person plural (*son*). Both *mediodía* (noon) and *medianoche* (midnight) take the third person singular form *es*. Emphasise that *y* (and) is used to express 'minutes past' the hour and *menos* (less) is used to express 'minutes to'. *En punto* means 'on the dot': for example, *Es la una en punto.* As a follow-up activity, ask questions such as *¿Cuántos segundos hay en un minuto?* (How many seconds are there in one minute?), *¿Cuántos minutos hay en una hora?* (How many minutes in one hour?)

Page 17 ¿Qué hora es? Revise asking and saying the time. For further practice, tell the children that each clock on the sheet is either five minutes fast (*adelantado*) or slow (*atrasado*). Invite them to say the real time in each case. As a further extension, practise adding more information into the dialogue with the expression *Es hora de* + infinitive (It's time to …): for example, *¿Qué hora es? Son las dos y media. Es hora de comer.*

Page 18 Una invitación Create a display-size invitation card for a birthday party or a carnival party. Follow the models on the activity sheet and include the date, the place and the time of the party. Show the children the card and ask questions such as *¿Para qué es la fiesta?* (What is the party for?), *¿Cuándo es la fiesta?* (When is the party?), *¿A qué hora es la fiesta?* (What time is the party?) Encourage those who have created their own invitations to read them aloud.

Los días de la semana

👁 **Mira la lista.**

🔤 **Ordena las letras.**

Lista
domingo
jueves
lunes
martes
miércoles
sábado
viernes

① Hoy es snule
_____

② Hoy es ramset
_____

③ Hoy es cosmiérle
_____

④ Hoy es seejuv
_____

⑤ Hoy es rivesen
_____

⑥ Hoy es badosá
_____

⑦ Hoy es gomodin
_____

Y ahora

Escribe el día que viene antes y después.

_____ lunes _____

_____ jueves _____

_____ domingo

Translation: *The days of the week. Look at the list. Put the letters in order. • Write the day that comes before and after.*

Teachers' note: This activity introduces the names of the days of the week. The jumbled days of the week are in order from Monday to Sunday. In Spanish the days of the week are not capitalised. Encourage the children to memorise the days of the week and to say them out loud.

Developing Spanish
Libro Tres
© A & C BLACK

Los meses del año

 Mira la lista.

Escribe los meses en orden.

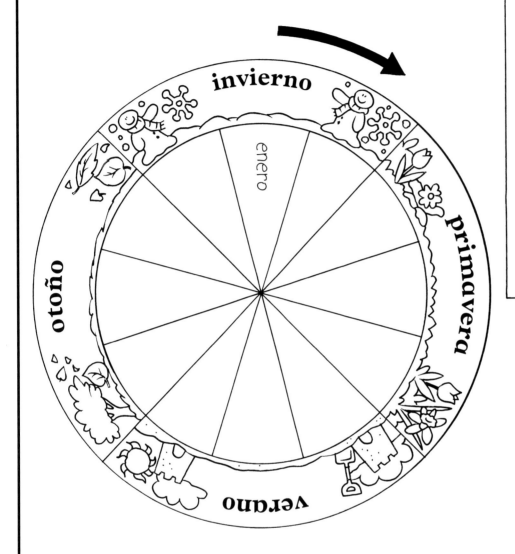

invierno

enero

primavera

otoño

verano

  Aprende el poema.

Treinta días tienen noviembre, abril, junio y septiembre.
De veintiocho hay sólo uno,
Los demás tienen treinta y uno.

Translation: *The months of the year. Look at the list. Write the months in order. • Learn the poem.*
Teachers' note: This activity introduces the months and seasons of the year. Go over the list to practise
pronunciation and ask the children to guess which month is which in English. The months of the year should
be written clockwise on the wheel, starting with *enero* (January). Encourage the children to memorise the
poem to help them to remember how many days each month has.

Developing Spanish
Libro Tres
© A & C BLACK

¿Qué fecha es hoy?

✏️ **Escribe la fecha.**

agosto 15

¿Qué fecha es hoy?

1) enero **1** — Es el primero de enero.

2) marzo **5** — _____

3) abril **14** — _____

4) junio **25** — _____

5) julio **11** — _____

6) septiembre **13** — _____

7) octubre **20** — _____

8) diciembre **1** — _____

Y ahora

✏️✏️ **Escribe la fecha de hoy en el calendario.**
Completa la frase.

Hoy _____

_____

Translation: *What's today's date? Write the date.* • *Write today's date on the calendar. Complete the sentence.*
Teachers' note: This activity provides practice in writing the date. Revise the months of the year and numbers up to 31. Point out that the first day of the month uses the ordinal *primero* rather than the cardinal number *uno*. For the extension activity the children must fill in the month and the date on the calendar and then write a complete sentence.

Developing Spanish
Libro Tres
© A & C BLACK

¡Feliz cumpleaños!

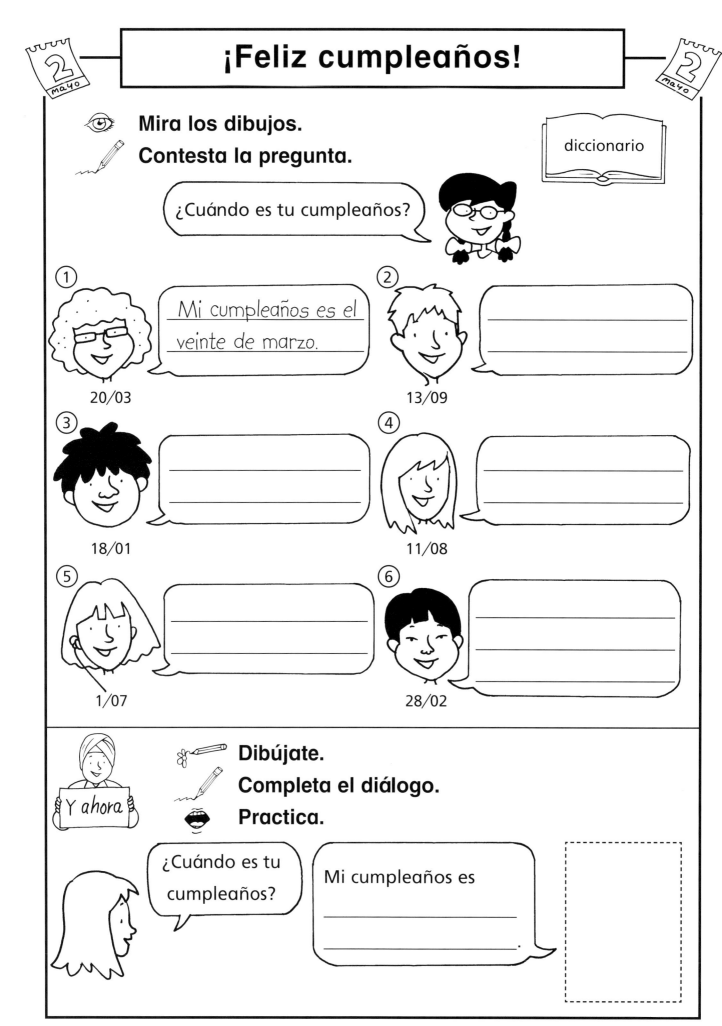

Mira los dibujos.

Contesta la pregunta.

diccionario

¿Cuándo es tu cumpleaños?

① Mi cumpleaños es el veinte de marzo.
20/03

②
13/09

③
18/01

④
11/08

⑤
1/07

⑥
28/02

Y ahora

Dibújate.

Completa el diálogo.

Practica.

¿Cuándo es tu cumpleaños?

Mi cumpleaños es

Translation: *Happy birthday! Look at the pictures. Answer the question. • Draw yourself. Complete the dialogue. Practise it.*

Teachers' note: This sheet uses the context of birthdays to develop the children's ability to write dates in words. Here they are given only the number cues. For the extension activity they must draw themselves, complete the speech bubble with their own information and then practise the dialogue with different partners.

Developing Spanish
Libro Tres
© **A & C BLACK**

Una fiesta española

 Lee la postal.

 Escoge la respuesta correcta.

diccionario

Pamplona
8 de julio

Querida abuela,
    Estoy en Pamplona para los Sanfermines, una fiesta emocionante y peligrosa. La ciudad cierra las calles y muchos toros corren detrás de jóvenes valientes. ¡Qué miedo!
    Besos,
        Pilar

María Rueda

Avenida Miraflores, 28

14810 Córdoba

1 ¿Quién escribe?	abuela	(Pilar)	María
2 ¿Dónde está Pilar?	Córdoba	Madrid	Pamplona
3 La fiesta es:	emocionante	valiente	interesante
4 Los toros:	caminan	bailan	corren
5 Pilar tiene:	frío	miedo	calor

Y ahora

Busca las palabras nuevas en el diccionario.

Escribe una lista en español y en inglés.

Ejemplo: *querida*   dear

Translation: *A Spanish festival. Read the postcard. Choose the correct answer. • Look up the new words in a dictionary. Write a list in Spanish and English.*
Teachers' note: This activity provides reading comprehension practice and encourages use of a bilingual dictionary. The children should first read through the text to try to work out the meaning. Use this as a starting point for discussing Spanish festivals and traditions.

Developing Spanish
Libro Tres
© A & C BLACK

La hora

 Corta las fichas.

 Pega las frases debajo de los dibujos.

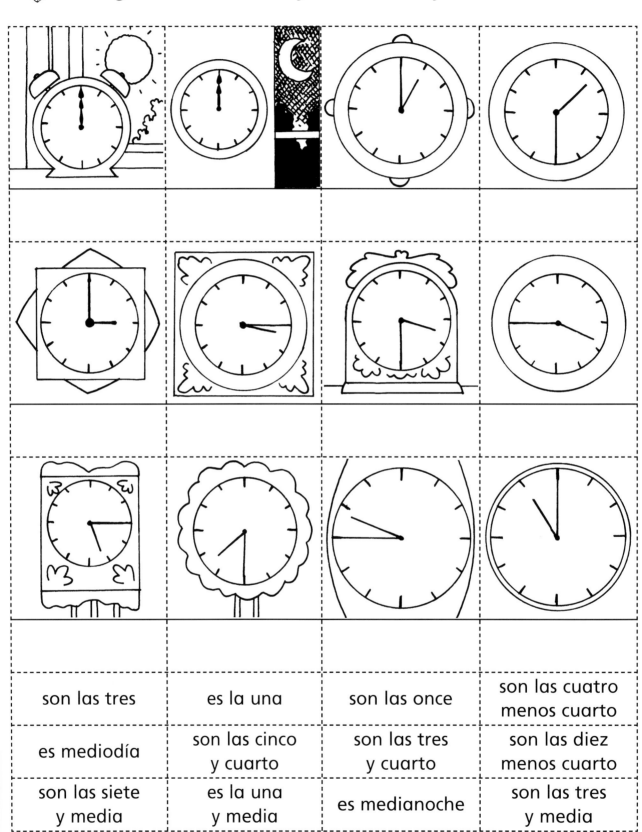

son las tres	es la una	son las once	son las cuatro menos cuarto
es mediodía	son las cinco y cuarto	son las tres y cuarto	son las diez menos cuarto
son las siete y media	es la una y media	es medianoche	son las tres y media

Translation: *Time. Cut out the cards. Glue the phrases under the drawings.*
Teachers' note: To make flashcards copy the sheet onto A3 card. This activity introduces the children to telling the time in Spanish. They should match the phrases and the pictures before gluing them together. Ask them to work in pairs, taking turns to quiz each other by showing a card to their partner, covering the words and asking *¿Qué hora es?* (What time is it?)

Developing Spanish
Libro Tres
© A & C BLACK

¿Qué hora es?

 Mira la lista.

Escribe la hora.

Lista

Es la una menos diez.

Es la una y cinco.

Son las dos y veinte.

Son las siete menos veinticinco.

Son las tres y veinticinco.

① 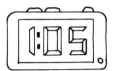 _____

② _____

③ _____

④  _____

⑤ _____

👄 **Practica el diálogo.**

Y ahora

¿Qué hora es?

11·55   4·10

5·15   6·00

Translation: *What time is it? Look at the list. Write the time. • Practise the dialogue.*
Teachers' note: This activity gives practice in writing the time. For the extension activity, put the children in pairs to practise asking and saying the different times. Extend this further by asking one child to say a time for their partner to write down in digits.

Developing Spanish
Libro Tres
© A & C BLACK

Una invitación

 Lee las invitaciones.

Contesta las preguntas.

¡Ven a mi fiesta de cumpleaños!

Cuándo: 20/05

Dónde: mi casa

Hora: 4:00

¿Cuándo es la fiesta?

_____

_____

¿A qué hora es la fiesta?

_____

_____

¡Fiesta de fin de año!

Cuándo: 15/06

Dónde: el gimnasio de la escuela

Hora: 5:30

¿Cuándo es la fiesta?

_____

_____

¿A qué hora es la fiesta?

_____

_____

Escribe una invitación.

Y ahora

Qué: _____

_____

Cuándo: _____

Dónde: _____

Hora: _____

Translation: *An invitation. Read the invitations. Answer the questions. • Write an invitation.*
Teachers' note: This activity revises writing dates and the time. Point out that *¿A qué hora es...?* means
'At what time is...?' when asking about schedules. Emphasise that the answers must be all in words. For
the extension activity the children should write their own invitation modelled on those above.

Developing Spanish
Libro Tres
© A & C BLACK

18

Topic 2: El tiempo

Key vocabulary

el tiempo	the weather
el pronóstico del tiempo	weather forecast
hace buen tiempo	it's fine weather
hace mal tiempo	it's bad weather
hace calor	it's hot
hace frío	it's cold
hace sol	it's sunny
hace viento	it's windy
llueve	it's raining
nieva	it's snowing
el abanico	fan
el abrigo	coat
las botas	boots
la bufanda	scarf
las gafas de sol	sunglasses
los guantes	gloves
el impermeable	raincoat
el jersey	jumper
el paraguas	umbrella
las sandalias	sandals
el sombrero	hat
el traje de baño	bathing suit
¿Por qué...?	Why...?
porque	because

Expressions

¿Qué tiempo hace?	What's the weather like?
¡De vacaciones!	On holiday!
¿Qué llevas cuando...?	What do you wear when...?

Teaching ideas

Vocabulary note
Introduce weather words and phrases with display-size copies of the cards on page 21. Refer to the weather outside and ask *¿Qué tiempo hace?* Show the corresponding flashcard and read the caption. Prompt the children to repeat the answer. Once they are familiar with the vocabulary spend a few minutes of every lesson talking about the weather.

To practise weather words in conjunction with the days of the week, create a poster headed *¿Qué tiempo hace hoy?* Write the days of the week down one side. Use the flashcards on page 21 to make labels to fix next to each day. Begin each lesson by asking *¿Qué día es hoy?* and *¿Qué tiempo hace hoy?* Ask a different child each day to fix the right weather card on the poster.

Picture dictionary
Use the Picture dictionary on pages 28 and 29 to revise weather conditions and clothing words. Ask questions such as *¿Dónde nieva?*, *¿Quién lleva una bufanda?*, *¿Quién tiene frío?*, *¿Qué tiempo hace?*, *¿Dónde está...?*

To make a classroom display enlarge the Picture dictionary and add labels such as *llueve*, *nieva*, *hace viento*, etc. To revise warm-weather vocabulary invite the children to make a seaside picture dictionary of their own with the appropriate weather conditions, clothing and activities.

Spanish culture
The following playground chant is recited by Spanish children on rainy days:

Que llueva, que llueva	Let it rain, let it rain
La vieja está en la cueva	The old woman is in the cave
Los pajaritos cantan	The little birds sing
La vieja se levanta.	The old woman gets up.

Prompt the children to compare the climate between the UK and Spain. In general, Spain has a temperate climate. The southern and eastern coasts have a Mediterranean climate with hot, dry summers and mild winters. Southern Spain also has the warmest weather in mainland Europe. Because it is warm there even in winter, it is a popular holiday destination. The western, Atlantic coast is cooler in summer and can have heavy rains in autumn and winter. The higher altitude central area of Spain, where Madrid is located, has a temperate climate and can be very cold in winter.

Notes on the activities

Page 21 El tiempo Present weather phrases using enlarged laminated copies of the symbols. Prompt the children to repeat the words to ensure proper pronunciation. Fix the symbols to a large wall map of Spain and say sentences such as *En Valencia hace buen tiempo*. Ask the children to make up symbols for *hace fresco* (it's cool/chilly), *está nublado* (it's cloudy), *hay niebla* (it's foggy) and for the nouns *el sol* (sun), *la nube* (cloud), *la lluvia* (rain), *la nieve* (snow), *el arco iris* (rainbow).

Page 22 ¿Qué tiempo hace? Revise weather phrases orally, then use this activity to practise the written form. Some children may be able to complete the sheet with the word bank masked. Mention that the present continuous forms *está lloviendo* and *está nevando* are common alternatives to *llueve* and *nieva*. As a further extension ask pairs of children to describe the weather using mime and guessing the answer. They could also practise the extension activity dialogue and keep changing the information. Tell them *llueve a cántaros* (it's raining jugfuls) is the Spanish equivalent of 'it's raining buckets'.

Page 23 El pronóstico del tiempo Give out atlases and draw a simple outline map of Spain on the blackboard. Call out some city names and ask volunteers to find them in their atlas and then mark them on the map. (Point out that Spain has land borders with France to the north-east and Portugal to the west. Ask the children to check their atlases and to mark Spain's coasts in blue and land borders in brown.) Stage a mock weather forecast. Ask the children to choose and fix weather flashcards for the forecast you call out: for example, *En Madrid llueve*. When all the flashcards are on the map ask questions such as *¿Qué tiempo hace en Bilbao?* Display an enlarged copy of a newspaper weather map for your area and invite a child to give the local weather forecast. The children can research what the actual weather is in a particular place in Spain by logging on to www.weather.co.uk.

Page 24 El tiempo y las estaciones Start with an oral revision activity by inviting the children to describe the weather shown in the pictures. Check that they are secure with the names of the seasons (see page 12). Follow up the exercise by asking them to correct the false sentence, which should read *En primavera hace buen tiempo*. For extra practice and revision discuss the changes in the seasons. Ask *¿Te gusta el invierno?* (Do you like the winter?), *¿Qué actividades se hacen en el verano?* (What activities are done in summer?) The book *El Tiempo* in the *Mundo Maravilloso* series (Ediciones SM) is helpful on seasonal weather changes.

Page 25 ¡De vacaciones! Begin by revising the words for everyday clothes from **Developing Spanish Libro Dos**, page 34. Then introduce the words for clothes particularly suited to hot and cold weather by showing real items of clothing or pictures cut from magazines and catalogues. Ask the children to divide them up according to whether they would be suitable for summer or winter holidays. Play the game *La maleta*, but start off by saying *Es verano* (or *Es invierno*). *Voy de vacaciones y en mi maleta llevo...*, using the names of suitable items of clothing. Refer to the weather map of Spain on page 23. Tell the children to choose a city to travel to and to make a list of the clothes they need to pack for a weekend holiday in that city according to the weather forecast.

Page 26 ¿Qué llevas...? Revise weather phrases and items of clothing with the help of the flashcards from page 21 and articles of clothing or pictures cut from catalogues: for example, hold up the cold weather card and ask *¿Qué llevas cuando hace frío?* Play a variation of *Simón dice...* by saying, for example, *Simón dice 'Es invierno, ponte una bufanda'* to prompt the children to mime putting on a scarf. If the season and the clothes item mentioned don't tally, they should ignore the command or be eliminated. For extra listening practice place in front of the class four photographs of people or groups of people cut from magazines (clothes advertisements work well). Describe one of the pictures. Talk about what the people look like and what items of clothing they are wearing. Give the children one piece of information at a time: for example: *En esta foto hay una niña. No hay un perro. La niña lleva una bufanda. La bufanda es roja.* The class must identify which picture you are describing.

Page 27 Sopa de letras del tiempo Play *El ahorcado* using weather vocabulary or write jumbled weather words on the board and invite the children to unscramble them. Once they have completed the activity, use the hidden words *MAR Y SOL* to prompt group discussion about why Spain is such a popular summer holiday destination: *¿Por qué va mucha gente a España para las vacaciones de verano?* Elicit answers such as *Porque hace mucho sol. Porque hace buen tiempo. Porque no llueve mucho.* Point out that parts of Spain, especially the centre and the north, can be very cold in winter.

To review the vocabulary and expressions presented in Topic 2, play word bingo. Provide the children with an empty 16-box grid. Ask them to write a word or expression from the activity sheets and the picture dictionary in each box. The children must cross out the words or phrases as you call them. Play first for four words in a row and then for the whole grid.

El tiempo

 Mira la lista.

Completa las fichas.

Colorea los dibujos.

Lista

hace buen tiempo	hace sol
hace calor	hace viento
hace frío	llueve
hace mal tiempo	nieva

_____

_____

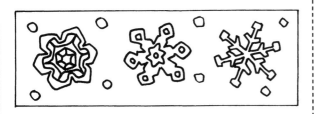

_____

_____

_____

_____

Translation: *The weather. Look at the list. Complete the cards.*
Teachers' note: To make flashcards enlarge the sheet to A3 and copy it onto card. This activity presents weather phrases. The children should colour the cards after writing the correct phrase under each picture. Use the cards for games such as Snap! and Pairs. The children can test each other by hiding either the words or the picture and asking a partner to say or draw the missing part.

Developing Spanish
Libro Tres
© A & C BLACK

¿Qué tiempo hace?

Mira la lista.

Completa el esquema.

Developing Spanish
Libro Tres
© A & C BLACK

Lista

hace calor
hace frío
hace sol
hace viento
llueve
nieva

¿Qué tiempo hace?

Completa el diálogo.

Y ahora

¿ _____ ?

Hace buen tiempo.

Translation: *What's the weather like?* Look at the list. Complete the chart. • *Complete the dialogue.*
Teachers' note: This activity introduces the question *¿Qué tiempo hace?* and practises writing weather
phrases. For the extension activity the children should complete the dialogue with the question *¿Qué
tiempo hace?* and practise the conversation using different weather vocabulary.

22

El pronóstico del tiempo

Lee las frases.

Dibuja el tiempo.

En Salamanca llueve.

En Cádiz hace calor.

En La Coruña hace frío.

En Bilbao hace viento.

En Sevilla hace buen tiempo.

En Valencia hace sol.

En Barcelona hace mal tiempo.

Mira el mapa.

Completa el diálogo.

Y ahora

¿Qué tiempo hace en Madrid?

Developing Spanish
Libro Tres
© A & C BLACK

El tiempo y las estaciones

 Mira la lista.

 Ordena las letras.

r v m r p i a e a

_____

a e v r n o

_____

ñ o t o o

_____

o r i n i v e n

_____

 Marca verdadero ✔ **o falso** ✗ .

En primavera nieva y hace viento. ☐ En otoño llueve y hace viento. ☐

En verano hace sol y hace calor. ☐ En invierno hace frío. ☐

 Dibuja tu estación preferida.

¿Qué tiempo hace?

Describe.

diccionario

Translation: *The weather and the seasons. Look at the list. Put the letters in order. Mark true or false.*
• *Draw your favourite season. What's the weather like? Describe it.*
Teachers' note: This activity combines revision of the four seasons and of describing the weather. After the children have drawn their favourite season for the extension activity, encourage them to describe it orally to the class or to a classmate.

Developing Spanish
Libro Tres
© A & C BLACK

¡De vacaciones!

Mira la lista.

Escribe las palabras en la maleta correcta.

Lista

el abrigo
las botas
la bufanda
la camiseta
las gafas de sol
los guantes
el jersey
los pantalones cortos
las sandalias
el traje de baño

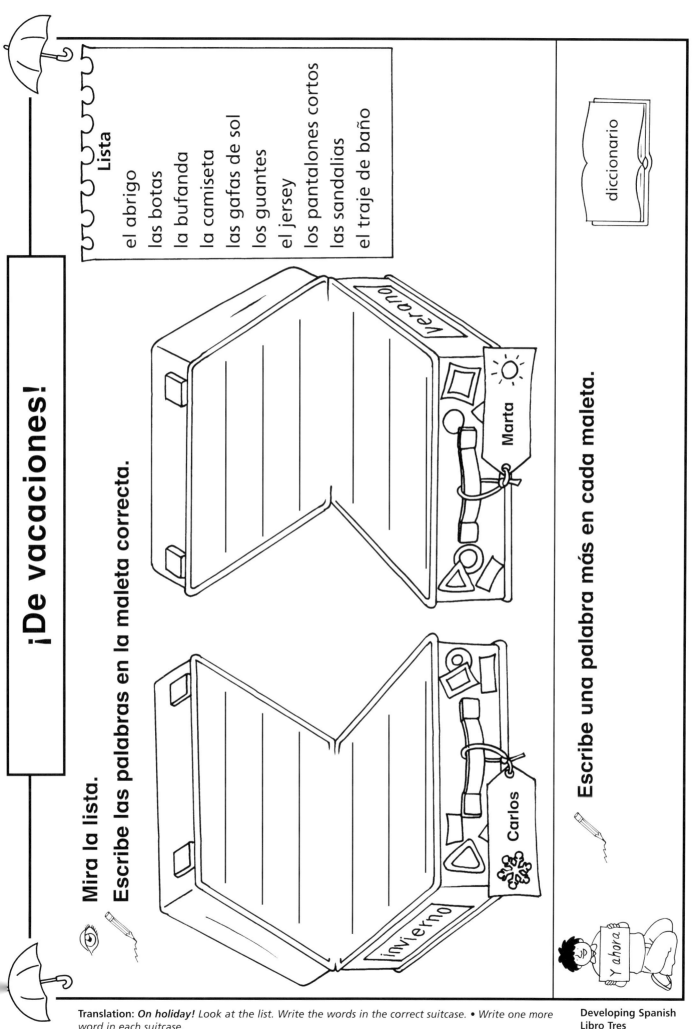

Verano

Marta

invierno

Carlos

diccionario

Escribe una palabra más en cada maleta.

Y ahora

Developing Spanish
Libro Tres
© A & C BLACK

25

Translation: *On holiday!* *Look at the list. Write the words in the correct suitcase. • Write one more word in each suitcase.*

Teachers' note: This activity introduces some weather-related clothes. Read the word bank together to ensure that the children understand the words and can pronounce them correctly. Encourage them to use a bilingual dictionary to look up other hot and cold weather clothes for the extension activity.

¿Qué llevas...?

 Une las frases con una línea.

diccionario

En primavera hace fresco.• • Llevo una bufanda.

En verano hace sol. • • Llevo un jersey.

En otoño llueve. • • Llevo unas gafas de sol.

En invierno hace frío. • • Llevo un impermeable.

Cuando llueve • • llevo botas.

Cuando hace frío • • llevo pantalones cortos.

Cuando hace calor • • llevo un abrigo.

Cuando nieva • • llevo un paraguas.

  ¿Qué lleva Marta en verano?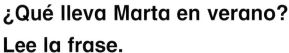
Lee la frase.
 Dibuja a Marta.

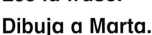 

En verano llevo un traje de baño y unas sandalias.

Translation: ***What do you wear...?*** *Draw a line to match the phrases.* • *What does Marta wear in the summer? Read the sentence. Draw Marta.*

Teachers' note: This activity combines the topics of weather and clothing. Check the children's answers orally by asking questions such as *¿Qué llevas en primavera?*

Developing Spanish
Libro Tres
© A & C BLACK

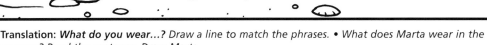

Sopa de letras del tiempo

 Mira la lista.

 Busca las palabras.

P	A	R	A	G	U	A	S	M	S
R	A	L	L	U	E	V	E	A	I
I	J	C	V	A	R	〰	T	Y	N
M	E	A	I	N	A	O	V	B	V
A	R	L	E	T	B	F	E	U	I
V	S	O	N	E	R	R	R	F	E
E	E	R	T	S	I	Í	A	A	R
R	Y	S	O	☀	G	O	N	N	N
A	O	L	O	T	O	Ñ	O	D	O
👓	S	A	N	D	A	L	I	A	S

 Busca las palabras escondidas.

☐ ☐ ☐ ☐ ☐ ☐ ☐

  Comenta el tiempo español.

Translation: *Weather wordsearch. Look at the list. Find the words.* • *Find the hidden words. Discuss Spanish weather.*

Teachers' note: This activity brings together weather and clothing vocabulary. The words in the grid are down, across or diagonal. Once the children have ringed all the words from the list, they will find seven unused letters which make the hidden words in the extension activity. Use them as a starting point for group discussion.

Developing Spanish
Libro Tres
© A & C BLACK

Picture dictionary

el cielo

el sol

la nube

la lluvia

la nieve

el arco iris

la montaña

el paraguas

las botas

el impermeable

el abrigo

28

Developing Spanish
Libro Tres
© A & C BLACK

¿Qué tiempo hace?

mojado

seco

tener frío

tener calor

nevar

la
bufanda

las gafas
de sol

la tienda

ponerse

escalar

hacer sol

Developing Spanish
Libro Tres
© A & C BLACK

29

Topic 3: La vida diaria

Key vocabulary

la vida diaria	daily life
yo desayuno	I eat breakfast
yo almuerzo	I eat lunch
yo ceno	I eat dinner
yo me levanto	I get up
yo me visto	I get dressed
yo me lavo	I wash
yo me cepillo los dientes	I brush my teeth
yo me cepillo el pelo	I brush my hair
yo voy a la escuela	I go to school
yo regreso a casa	I return home
yo juego	I play
yo hago los deberes	I do homework
yo me baño	I have a bath
yo me ducho	I have a shower
yo me acuesto	I go to bed
yo me duermo	I go to/fall asleep
el horario	timetable
el sondeo	survey

Expressions

¿A qué hora...?	At what time...?
¿Qué hace...?	What is ... doing?
¿Cada cuánto?	How often?

Grammar

- reflexive verbs, e.g. *lavarse*:
  yo me lavo
  tú te lavas
  él/ella se lava

- adverbs of frequency: *siempre* (always), *normalmente* (normally), *a veces* (sometimes), *nunca* (never)

Teaching ideas

Vocabulary note
This topic introduces some common reflexive verbs. Help the children to understand that some Spanish verbs need a reflexive pronoun (*me, te, se, nos, os*) because they express what people do to or for themselves. Point out that they are already familiar with this type of verb because they know the expressions *¿Cómo te llamas?* and *Yo me llamo...* Use your own daily routine to present these verbs: for example, *Yo me levanto, me lavo la cara,* etc.

The reflexive verbs in this topic are introduced in the first three persons singular: *yo me levanto, tú te levantas, usted/él/ella se levanta.* The pronoun *se* is used for both masculine and feminine subjects. Point out that in the infinitive these verbs have a 'special' *-se* ending attached to the verb: for example, *levantarse, vestirse, cepillarse.* To help the children to recognise them, ask them to colour-code the phrases containing reflexive verbs on the flashcards on page 32.

Picture dictionary
Use the Picture dictionary on pages 38 and 39 to introduce or to revise the vocabulary in this topic. Ask questions such as *¿Quién se levanta?* (Who is getting up?), *¿Quién desayuna?* (Who is having breakfast?) Prompt the children to describe the picture either orally or in writing by asking about the time, the temperature, the weather and what people are wearing. Revise the verb *estar* (to be) which is used to describe where people or things are (see **Developing Spanish Libro Uno**, pages 40 and 47). Explain that it is also used to describe temporary states or situations. For practice with this usage, ask questions including adjectives: *¿Quién está sucio?* (Who is dirty?), *¿Quién está dormido?* (Who is asleep?)

Spanish culture
When learning about daily routines the children might enjoy knowing about typical school timetables in Spain. These do vary, but in general, school hours are from 9 am to 5 pm with a two-hour lunch break. With such a long lunch break children usually have the option to go home and have lunch with their families and perhaps a traditional *siesta* (afternoon nap). An alternative school schedule is from 9 am to 2 pm with no lunch break. School is usually Monday to Friday.

Shops also have a long break in the afternoon. They are generally open to the public from 9 am to 1.30 or 2 pm and then re-open from 4.30 or 5 until 8 pm. To express 'from ... to ...' when talking about schedules, use *desde ... hasta ...*: for example, *La zapatería está abierta desde las nueve hasta la una y media.*

Notes on the activities

Page 32 Acciones habituales Introduce phrases for describing daily routine through mime or using enlarged copies of the flashcards. Once the children are familiar with these expressions, they can make extra cards for phrases such as *Yo me cepillo el pelo* (I brush my hair), *Yo me baño* (I have a bath), *Yo me duermo* (I go to sleep), *Yo toco el piano* (I play the piano), etc. Ask them to stick all their cards in order on a sheet of A3 paper to represent their daily routine and create a personalised poster. Encourage them to present their posters by using *por la mañana* (in the morning), *por la tarde* (in the afternoon) and *por la noche* (in the evening/at night) to say when they do things. The children could use the phrases they have learned to write their own daily journal.

Page 33 Las actividades diarias Revise telling the time (see pages 16–17). Ask the children to look at the digital displays in the pictures and to say which is the earliest time and which is the latest. Explain that in Spain official times (timetables, appointments, etc.) are given using a 24-hour clock but in everyday conversation people use a 12-hour clock and specify the time of day using *de la mañana*, *de la tarde* and *de la noche*. Point out that 'in the morning' etc. is translated in two ways in Spanish according to whether the sentence is specifying an exact time: *Voy al colegio por la mañana* (I go to school in the morning) but *Voy al colegio a las ocho de la mañana* (I go to school at 8 o'clock in the morning). As a follow-up activity, play a variation of *¡Qué confusión!* (see page 7): read out one of the sentences from the cards but change the verb or the time.

Page 34 ¿A qué hora? On small pieces of paper, write questions using *¿A qué hora…?* similar to those on the activity sheet. Distribute one question to each child. Prompt the children to read and answer their question aloud. Once they have completed the sheet, divide them into pairs to practise the dialogues shown in the activity. As a follow-up, invite the children to write a short description of their own schedule on a typical day.

Page 35 Mi horario Revise the days of the week (see page 11) and school subjects (see **Developing Spanish Libro Uno**, page 24). After the children have completed the sheet, divide them into pairs to ask each other questions to obtain information: *¿A qué hora tienes historia?*, *¿Qué día tienes historia?*, *¿Qué tienes los jueves?*, *¿Qué tienes el lunes a las nueve?* Suggest they create a timetable for the weekend and present it to the class.

Page 36 ¿Qué hace…? Begin by asking a child *¿Qué haces a las cuatro de la tarde?* (What do you do at 4 pm?) Repeat his or her reply in the third person using the child's name: for example, *Paul regresa a casa a las cuatro de la tarde*. Emphasise the verb form with voice and gesture. Repeat with other children and different verbs. Divide the children into pairs and ask them to make up and write sentences about either Marta's or Carlos's daily routine, including times. When the children are ready, ask the pairs to come up to the front of the class. One child is the narrator (*el narrador/la narradora*) and the other is either Marta or Carlos. The narrator reads one sentence at a time while the other mimes the actions. To finish off ask the children what they do. Some children may be able to ask and respond to questions using plural verb forms: for example, *¿Qué hacéis vosotros a las seis de la mañana?* (What do you do at six o'clock in the morning?), *¿Qué hacen los chicos a las doce y media?* (What do the children do at half past twelve?)

Page 37 Un sondeo To introduce adverbs of frequency draw a vertical line on the board with a plus sign at the top and a minus sign at the bottom. Write *siempre* next to the plus sign and *nunca* next to the minus sign. In between, starting at the top, write *normalmente* and *a veces*. Say sentences such as *Me gusta correr. Yo corro todos los días. Siempre corro* (I like running. I run every day. I always run). Stress the word *siempre*. Express the opposite by saying sentences such as *No me gusta jugar al baloncesto. Nunca juego al baloncesto* (I don't like playing basketball. I never play basketball). Ask the children if they can guess what *normalmente* (usually) and *a veces* (sometimes) mean. Once they have completed the sheet, ask questions starting *¿Cada cuánto…?* (How often…?) using the sentences in the activity. The children must give complete answers using the adverb of frequency of their choice. Suggest that the class collate everyone's information and make a graph during ICT. Note that in Spanish adverbs of frequency can be placed in different positions in the sentence without changing the meaning: for example, *Siempre bebo té* and *Bebo té siempre* are both acceptable. *Nunca* can stand alone at the beginning of a sentence (*Nunca bebo té*) or be used in conjunction with the negative *no* in the construction *No bebo té nunca*.

Acciones habituales

 Corta las fichas.

 Pega las frases debajo de los dibujos.

yo me cepillo los dientes	yo almuerzo	yo me visto	yo regreso a casa
yo juego	yo me lavo	yo hago los deberes	yo desayuno
yo me levanto	yo voy a la escuela	yo me acuesto	yo ceno

Translation: *Regular habits.* Cut out the cards. Glue the phrases under the drawings.
Teachers' note: Copy the sheet onto A3 card. This activity introduces phrases describing daily routine. Ask the children to match the pictures and the phrases before gluing them together. Invite them to put the cards in the order in which they do these activities during a typical day. Encourage them to read the sequence of activities aloud.

Developing Spanish
Libro Tres
© A & C BLACK

Las actividades diarias

 Corta las fichas.

Juega dominó.

Yo ceno a las nueve de la noche.	7:05	Yo hago los deberes a las cinco de la tarde.	22:30
Yo me acuesto a las diez y media de la noche.	7:00	Yo me levanto a las siete de la mañana.	7:25
Yo voy a la escuela a las ocho menos cuarto.	21:00	Yo juego al baloncesto a las cuatro de la tarde.	7:30
Yo desayuno a las siete y veinticinco.	7:45	Yo me visto a las siete y cuarto de la mañana.	16:00
Yo almuerzo a la una de la tarde.	17:00	Yo regreso a casa a las tres y media de la tarde.	7:15
Yo me cepillo los dientes a las siete y media.	13:00	Yo me lavo a las siete y cinco de la mañana.	15:30

Translation: *Daily activities. Cut out the cards. Play dominoes.*
Teachers' note: This activity combines descriptions of daily routine with telling the time. The children should match each sentence to its corresponding picture. Point out that the sentences use a 12-hour clock and specify the part of the day while the digital displays use the 24-hour clock often found in Spain. Dominoes can be played individually or in pairs.

Developing Spanish
Libro Tres
© A & C BLACK

¿A qué hora?

 Mira la lista.

Completa los diálogos.

①

¿A qué hora te levantas?

Yo _____ a las seis y media.

②

¿_____ vas a la escuela?

Yo _____ a la escuela a las ocho menos cuarto.

③

¿_____ haces los deberes?

Yo _____ los deberes a las cinco menos diez.

④

¿_____ te acuestas?

Yo _____ a las nueve y media.

¿A qué hora te levantas?

Completa la frase.

Yo _____

_____

Translation: *At what time? Look at the list. Complete the dialogues.* • *What time do you get up? Complete the sentence.*

Teachers' note: This activity revises finding out at what times daily actions are done. For the extension activity the children should respond with a complete sentence following the models above. Encourage them to read their answers out loud.

Developing Spanish
Libro Tres
© A & C BLACK

Mi horario

Lista

almuerzo	inglés
arte	matemáticas
ciencias naturales	música
educación física	religión
español	
geografía	
historia	
informática	

Mira la lista.

Completa el horario con la hora y la actividad.

diccionario

Hora → Día ↓							
lunes							
martes							
miércoles							
jueves							
viernes							

¿Cuándo tienes español?
Contesta con una frase completa.

Y ahora

Translation: *My timetable. Look at the list. Fill in the timetable with the time and the activity.*
• When do you have Spanish? Answer with a complete sentence.

Teachers' note: This activity revises telling the time, the days of the week and school subjects. The children must complete the chart with their personal information. They should use a bilingual dictionary to look up any words not included in the word bank that they might need.

Developing Spanish
Libro Tres
© A & C BLACK

¿Qué hace...?

 Mira los dibujos.

 Mira la lista.

🖊 **Completa las frases.**

Lista
desayuna
duerme
hace monopatín
regresa a casa
ve la tele

① Son _las siete._ . Marta _duerme_ .

② Son _____ . José _____ .

③ Son _____ . Pilar _____ .

④ Son _____ . Felipe _____ .

⑤ Son _____ . Carla _____ .

⑥ Son _____ . Julio _____ .

🖊 **Ordena las palabras.**

corre   y   A   Tomás   cinco   las   ocho

_____

Translation: *What is ... doing? Look at the pictures. Look at the list. Complete the sentences.* • *Put the words in order.*

Teachers' note: This activity revises time phrases and helps the children to recognise the third person singular of the present tense of some verbs. Check their answers by asking questions such as *¿Qué hace José a las siete y cuarto?*

Developing Spanish
Libro Tres
© A & C BLACK

Un sondeo

¿Cada cuánto?
Lee las frases.
Marca ✔.

diccionario

	siempre	normalmente	a veces	nunca
Me levanto a las seis.				
Desayuno a las siete.				
Bebo leche.				
Almuerzo a las doce.				
Hago los deberes.				
En invierno esquío.				
Voy al cole a pie.				
Veo la tele por la tarde.				
Me acuesto temprano.				
Duermo diez horas.				

Y ahora

Completa las frases.

_____ llevo gafas de sol.

_____ voy a la escuela los domingos.

_____ ceno a las nueve de la noche.

_____ me acuesto a medianoche.

**Developing Spanish
Libro Tres**
© A & C BLACK

37

Picture dictionary

la hora

la temperatura

el reloj

el despertador

la izquierda

la derecha

el desayuno

el periódico

bañarse

levantarse

desayunar

Developing Spanish
Libro Tres
© A & C BLACK

¡Buenos días!

atrasado

sucio

limpio

dormido

esperar

 ver la tele

 ir a la escuela

 ir al trabajo

 cerrar

 abrir

 correr

Developing Spanish
Libro Tres
© A & C BLACK

Topic 4: La tecnología y el medio ambiente

Key vocabulary

la tecnología y el medio ambiente	technology and the environment
el concurso	quiz show
el control remoto	remote control
los dibujos animados	cartoons
el documental	documentary
la parabólica	satellite dish
la película	film
el programa	programme
el telediario	news bulletin
la telenovela	soap opera
la televisión	television
el televisor	television set
educativo/a	educational
informativo/a	informative
interesante	interesting
el ordenador	computer
el correo electrónico	e-mail
la impresora	printer
el mensaje	message
el monitor	monitor
la pantalla	screen
el portátil	laptop
el ratón	mouse
el teclado	keyboard
navegar en internet	to surf the net
el medio ambiente	the environment
el reciclaje	recycling
la basura	rubbish
el vidrio	glass
el papel	paper
el plástico	plastic
la botella (de agua, de champú, de detergente, de vino)	(water, shampoo, detergent, wine) bottle
el cartón	cardboard
el catálogo	catalogue
el contenedor	container
el folleto	leaflet
el frasco	small bottle
el periódico	newspaper
la revista	magazine
el tarro	jar
mantener	to keep
reciclar	to recycle
recoger	to pick up
respetar	to respect
tirar	to throw away

Expressions

¿Diga?	Hello?
¿Está ..., por favor?	Is ... there, please?
No, se ha equivocado.	Wrong number.
No, no está.	He/She is not here.
Sí, soy yo.	Speaking.
Sí. Un momento, ahora se pone.	Yes, just a minute. Here he/she is.
¿Qué te parece?	What do you think?

Teaching ideas

Use of technology

Discuss with the children how technology helps people to communicate. Explain that technology is a useful tool when learning a foreign language. Point out that DVDs offer a language choice. Suggest that the children watch their favourite films in Spanish. If possible, visit Spanish websites with the children – see page 62. You could set up an e-mail exchange with a class in Spain through the Internet.

Vocabulary note

Children enjoy using 'emoticons' when writing e-mails. To create these they need to know some punctuation marks: (:) *dos puntos*, (-) *raya*, (( )) *paréntesis*, (;) *punto y coma*. Ask them if they are familiar with these signs and understand what they mean. In Spanish the @ symbol used in e-mail addresses is called *arroba* and the dot is called *punto*.

Notes on the activities

Page 42 ¿Diga? Make sure the children understand the words on the list and can pronounce them correctly. Ask pairs of children to read the dialogues aloud. Encourage those children who have tackled the extension activity to role-play their dialogues in front of the class. As a follow-up, the children could practise leaving/taking a phone message:

—*¿Está José?* (Is José there?)
—*No, no está.* (No, he's not here.)
—*¿Puedo dejarle un mensaje?* (Can I leave him a message?)
—*Sí. Dime.* (Yes. Tell me.)

Page 43 La televisión Introduce types of television programmes by showing the children a Spanish television guide. You can download a current guide from a Spanish newspaper from a website such as http://www.elpais.es/gente.html#inicioparrilla. Ask the children to look at the words on the list in pairs and try to work out their meaning. For the extension activity they should write their answers first and then share them with the class. You may need to review numbers and telling the time. As a follow-up activity, ask them to make up Spanish titles for each of the programmes in the main activity. Promote intercultural discussion by asking the children to compare the programmes from the Spanish TV guide with their local programming. Explain that *tele* is short for *televisión* and is the familiar way of referring to television.

Page 44 ¿Qué te parece? Tell the children that they are going to learn some adjectives to help them to express their personal opinions. Introduce the question *¿Qué te parece?* (What do you think?) and explain that when it is followed by a noun such as *el programa* it means 'What do you think about the programme?' Point out that if the noun is plural the verb form changes to agree: for example, *¿Qué te parecen los programas?* (What do you think about the programmes?) Make sure the children understand the meanings of the adjectives on the list, then read through the questions together and encourage oral answers. Remind them that the verb and adjective forms in their answers should reflect the number and gender of the corresponding programmes: for example, *¿Qué te parecen las telenovelas? Me parecen divertidas.* Compare the children's answers and ask them why they find certain types of programmes interesting or boring: *¿Por qué te parece interesante/aburrido este tipo de programa?* Broaden the discussion to compare the children's attitudes towards television, reading and physical activity. Encourage them to think about the health implications of watching too much TV. Some children may be able to express their opinion using the construction *Me parece que…* (I think that…) Ask them to rewrite their answers in the extension activity to open with this phrase: *Me parece que leer es …*

Page 45 El ordenador Link this activity with an ICT lesson. Read through the word bank and ask the children if they can recognise or guess any of the meanings from the English. Create large labels (or use sticky notes) showing the words on the list. (Include *el portátil* only if a laptop computer is available in school.) Ask volunteers to attach the labels to the appropriate parts and accessories of a real computer, saying each word aloud. Remove the labels and distribute them to pairs of children. Ask one child to say the word while his or her partner re-attaches the label to the right part of the computer. As a follow-up discussion, ask the children questions such as *¿Tienes un ordenador en casa?* (Do you have a computer at home?), *¿Es portátil?* (Is it a laptop?), *¿Dónde está?* (Where is it?), *¿Cada cuánto lo usas?* (How often do you use it?)

Page 46 Un correo electrónico Discuss with the children what they use a computer for – *hacer los deberes* (doing homework), *jugar* (playing), *escribir un correo electrónico* (writing e-mails), *navegar en internet* (surfing the Internet), *buscar información* (searching for information). Read the e-mail heading on the sheet together and ensure that the children understand who is sending and who is receiving the e-mail. Once they have completed the activity, ask them to correct the false sentences orally. Some children may be able to write a brief e-mail response from Paco to Carlos's message.

Page 47 ¡Reciclemos! Create three recycling containers using cardboard boxes or large paper bags. Label them *papel*, *plástico* and *vidrio*. Using real objects that are ready to be thrown away (except for glass – see below), invite the children to recycle them (*¡Reciclemos!*). Distribute the objects and ask them to place them in the correct container: for example, *Pon la botella de agua en el contenedor de plástico* (Put the water bottle in the container for plastic) or *¿Adónde va el catálogo? ¿Va en el contenedor de papel?* (Where does the catalogue go? Does it go in the container for paper?) For safety reasons, use pictures of glass objects cut out of magazines and supermarket advertisements rather than real glass objects. Link this activity to PSHE: create a recycling corner in the classroom with containers for plastic and paper. Ask the children to create a poster headed *¡Reciclemos!* to designate the area. They could also make Spanish labels for the containers.

Page 48 El medio ambiente Using an enlarged copy of the Picture dictionary on pages 28 and 29 discuss what we should or should not do in order to protect the environment. Write the headings *hacer* and *no hacer* on the board. Ask the children to share their ideas. Write each idea for action using the infinitive form of the verb under the appropriate heading: for example, *no recoger flores*, *no tirar la basura en el mar*, *reciclar el papel*. As a follow-up to the extension activity, encourage the children to write a rule to match the sign they have drawn. Display the signs in class or around the school.

Page 49 Crucigrama Revise television, computer and environment vocabulary by playing *La maleta* (see pages 6–7). The activity sheet can be used for revision or for a vocabulary quiz. As a follow-up activity invite the children to list each word from the crossword, adding its definite article, and then to make up a sentence containing the word.

¿Diga?

👁 **Mira la lista.**

✏ **Completa los diálogos.**

¿Diga?

1. ¿_____? — ¿Está Pancho?

2. ¿_____, por favor? — Sí, soy yo.

3. ¿Está José, ____ _____? — No, ____ _____.

4. ¿____ María, por favor? — Sí. ____ _____, ahora se pone.

5. ¿____ el Sr. Ruiz, por favor? — No, ____ ____ _____.

Trabaja con un/a compañero/a.

👄 **Inventa un diálogo por teléfono.**

Y ahora

Translation: *Hello? Look at the list. Complete the dialogues. • Work with a partner. Invent a telephone conversation.*

Teachers' note: This activity introduces expressions used when making a telephone call. In the extension activity, encourage the children to make up at least three sentences for each person. They can add greetings, suggestions or invitations or any other vocabulary they know.

**Developing Spanish
Libro Tres
© A & C BLACK**

La televisión

 Mira la lista.

Escribe las palabras debajo de los dibujos.

Lista

el concurso	la parabólica
el control remoto	la película
los dibujos animados	el telediario
el documental	la telenovela

Hermanos Sáez • Artículos Electrónicos

el televisor

Contesta las preguntas.

¿Cuál es tu programa preferido?

¿Qué tipo de programa es?

¿Cuántas horas de tele ves al día?

Y ahora

Translation: *Television. Look at the list. Write the words under the pictures. • Answer the questions.*
Teachers' note: This activity introduces television-related vocabulary, including the words for TV set, satellite dish and remote control and for different types of programmes. The extension activity provides the children with an opportunity to write about their viewing habits and programme preferences.

Developing Spanish
Libro Tres
© A & C BLACK

43

¿Qué te parece?

 Mira la lista.

Contesta las preguntas.

¿Qué te parecen los documentales?

Me parecen educativos.

¿Qué te parecen los concursos?

_____
_____

¿Qué te parece el telediario?

_____
_____

¿Qué te parecen los dibujos animados?

_____
_____

¿Qué te parecen las películas de acción?

_____
_____

Y ahora

¿Qué te parece?

Completa las frases.

Ver la televisión es _____

Leer es _____

Practicar un deporte es _____

Translation: *What do you think? Look at the list. Answer the questions.* • *What do you think? Complete the sentences.*

Teachers' note: This activity gives the children an opportunity to express their personal opinions about TV programmes. They should choose an adjective that best expresses their view and make sure it agrees in number and gender with the noun it describes in each answer.

Developing Spanish
Libro Tres
© A & C BLACK

El ordenador

Mira el dibujo.
Mira la lista.
Escribe las etiquetas.

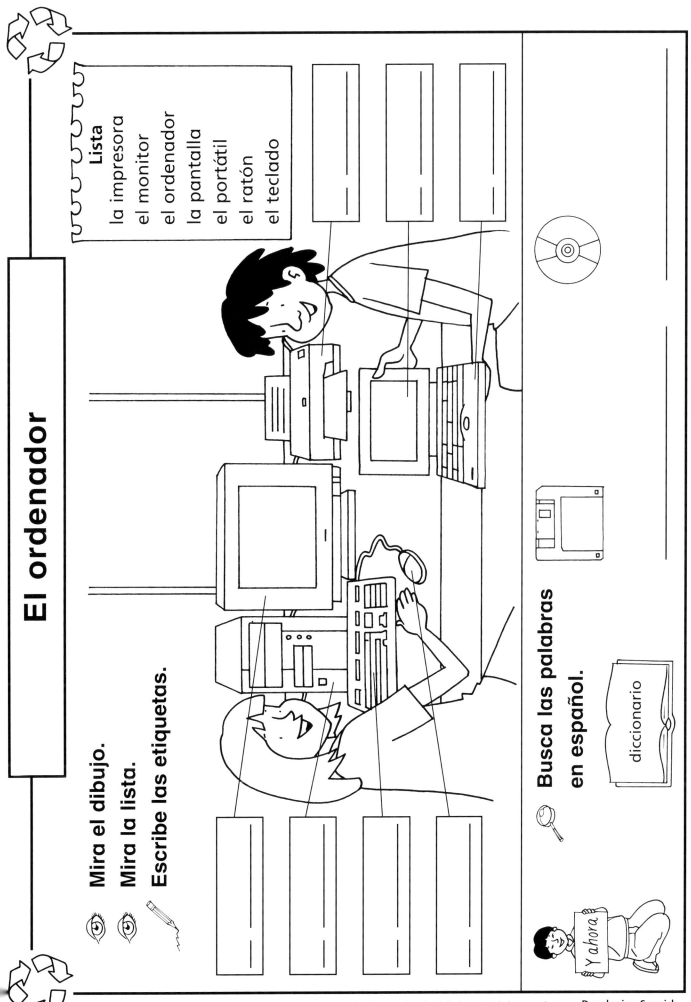

Lista
la impresora
el monitor
el ordenador
la pantalla
el portátil
el ratón
el teclado

diccionario

Busca las palabras en español.

Y ahora

Developing Spanish
Libro Tres
© A & C BLACK

Un correo electrónico

Lee el mensaje.

Lee las frases.

Marca verdadero ✔ **o falso** ✗ .

diccionario

De: carlos@correo.es

Para: paco@correo.es

Tema: ¡Finalmente!

¡Hola Paco!

Hoy es mi cumpleaños y ¡qué sorpresa! :-)

¡Finalmente tengo un ordenador nuevo!

También tengo una impresora. Ahora puedo navegar en internet, escribir correo electrónico e imprimir mis fotos.

¿Puedes venir a mi casa este sábado a las tres de la tarde para jugar y usar mi ordenador nuevo?

Ahora tengo que estudiar historia. :-(

¡Hasta pronto!

Carlos

---

1 Paco tiene un ordenador nuevo. ☐

2 Este sábado es el cumpleaños de Carlos. ☐

3 Carlos puede navegar en internet. ☐

4 Carlos invita a Paco a su casa. ☐

Y ahora

Comprensión.

Escribe las respuestas.

1 ¿A qué hora invita a Paco a su casa?

2 ¿Qué asignatura tiene que estudiar Carlos?

Translation: *An e-mail. Read the message. Read the sentences. Mark true or false. • Comprehension. Write the answers.*

Teachers' note: This True or False activity revises some computer-related words. The children should read through the text first and look up any words they do not know. Some children may be able to answer the comprehension questions in the extension activity. Encourage them to answer in complete sentences.

**Developing Spanish
Libro Tres
© A & C BLACK**

¡Reciclemos!

✂ **Corta las fichas.**

✎ **Pega las fichas en el contenedor correcto.**

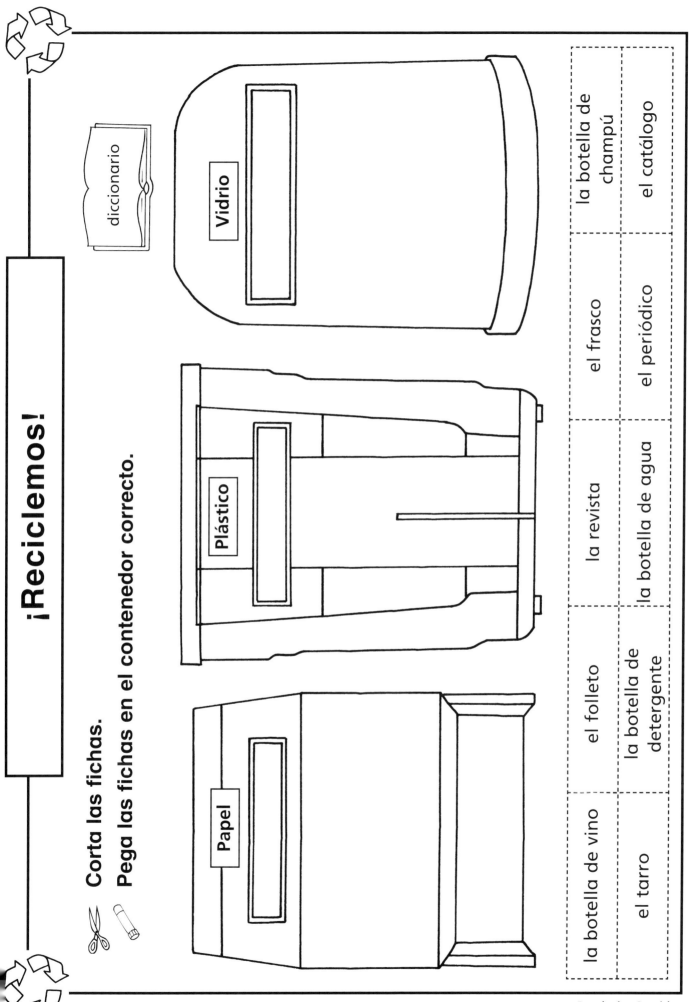

diccionario

Vidrio

Plástico

Papel

la botella de champú	el catálogo
el frasco	el periódico
la revista	la botella de agua
el folleto	la botella de detergente
la botella de vino	el tarro

Translation: *Let's recycle! Cut out the cards. Glue the cards on the correct container.*
Teachers' note: Enlarge the sheet to A3. This activity introduces words related to recycling. The children should classify the labels into objects made of *papel*, *plástico* and *vidrio* before gluing them on the containers. As an extension, ask the children to think of other recyclable materials (*aluminio*, *cartón*) and to draw, label and 'fill' containers for objects made of these.

Developing Spanish
Libro Tres
© A & C BLACK

El medio ambiente

 Une con una línea las
frases y los carteles.

diccionario

• No recoger las flores •

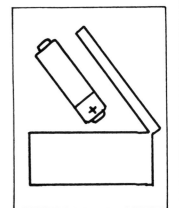

• Respetar los animales •

• No tirar botellas de
plástico en el mar •

• No tirar la basura •

• Tirar las pilas en
el contenedor correcto •

• Mantener limpia la ciudad •

Y ahora

 Dibuja otro cartel.

Translation: *The environment.* *Join the sentences and the signs.* • *Draw another sign.*
Teachers' note: This activity introduces some simple rules relating to respect for the environment. The
children can use a bilingual dictionary to look up any unfamiliar words. For the extension activity give the
children a large sheet of paper on which to draw a sign banning an activity that is bad for the environment.

**Developing Spanish
Libro Tres
© A & C BLACK**

Crucigrama

Escribe las palabras.

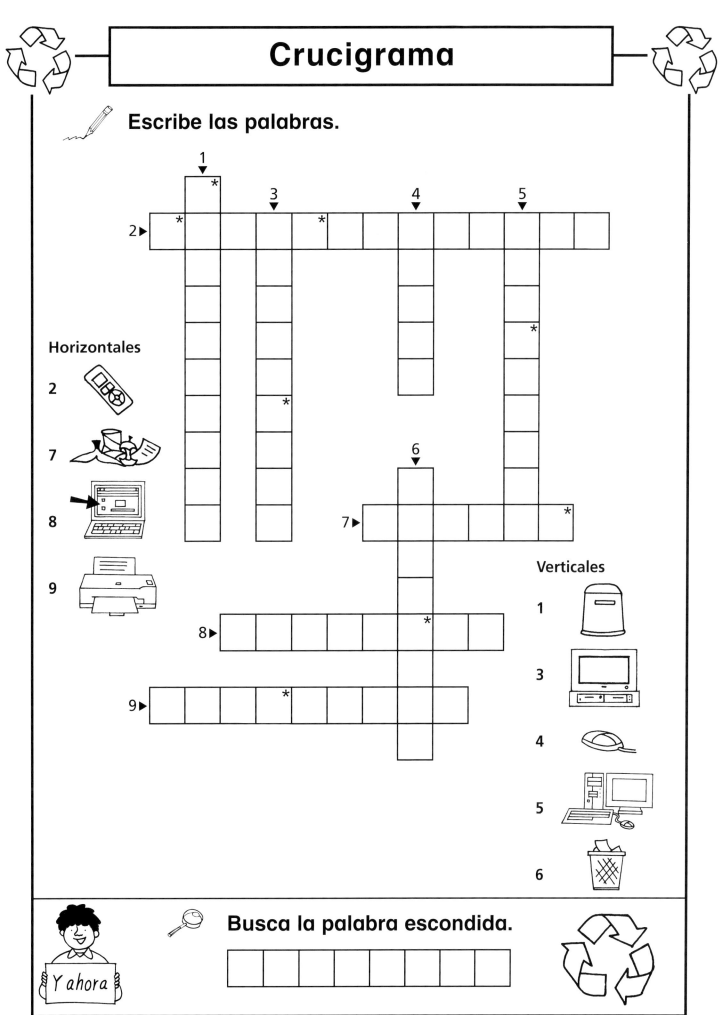

Horizontales

2

7

8

9

Verticales

1

3

4

5

6

Busca la palabra escondida.

Y ahora

Translation: **Crossword.** *Write the words.* • *Find the hidden word.*
Teachers' note: This activity revises many of the words from this topic. The children should rearrange the letters marked with an asterisk to find the hidden verb in the extension activity. Point out that the symbol alongside the boxes is a clue.

Developing Spanish
Libro Tres
© A & C BLACK

Topic 5: España y el mundo

Key vocabulary

España y el mundo	Spain and the world
la aldea	village
el/la artista	artist
el autor, la autora	author
el baile	dance
la capital	capital city
la corrida	bullfight
la dirección	address
la firma	signature
los habitantes	inhabitants
el kilómetro (Km.)	kilometre
la literatura	literature
el mapa	map
el pasaporte	passport
el pueblo	town
el toro	bull
la tradición	tradition
vivir	to live
los puntos cardinales	points of the compass
norte	North
sur	South
este	East
oeste	West
las nacionalidades	nationalities
los países	countries
Alemania, alemán/ana	Germany, German
Brasil, brasileño/a	Brazil, Brazilian
China, chino/a	China, Chinese
Egipto, egipcio/a	Egypt, Egyptian
Escocia, escocés/esa	Scotland, Scottish
España, español(a)	Spain, Spanish
Estados Unidos, estadounidense	United States, American
Francia, francés/esa	France, French
Gales, galés/esa	Wales, Welsh
Grecia, griego/a	Greece, Greek
India, indio/a	India, Indian
Inglaterra, inglés/esa	England, English
Irlanda, irlandés/esa	Ireland, Irish
Italia, italiano/a	Italy, Italian
Méjico, mejicano/a	Mexico, Mexican
Portugal, portugués/esa	Portugal, Portuguese
Rusia, ruso/a	Russia, Russian
Suiza, suizo/a	Switzerland, Swiss
Tailandia, tailandés/esa	Thailand, Thai
los continentes	continents
África	Africa
América	America
Asia	Asia
Europa	Europe
Oceanía	Australasia

numbers over 1,000: *mil* (1.000), *mil uno* (1.001), *mil cien* (1.100), *dos mil* (2.000), *diez mil* (10.000), *diez mil doscientos* (10.200), *cien mil* (100.000), *ciento cincuenta mil* (150.000), *quinientos mil* (500.000), *un millón* (1.000.000), *dos millones* (2.000.000), *un billón* (1.000.000.000)

Expressions

de ... a ...	from ... to ... (place)
¿De dónde eres?	Where are you from?
Yo soy de...	I'm from...
¿Dónde vives tú?	Where do you live?
¡Buen viaje!	Have a good trip!
'Todo el mundo es país'	'It's a small world'

Teaching ideas

Vocabulary note

To help the children to learn the names of countries and nationalities, use a world map or a globe. If the map is in English, replace place names with labels in Spanish. Create a classroom poster or display highlighting those countries in which Spanish is the main language. Include capital cities, flags, adjectives of nationality and population figures (to revise large numbers).

Picture dictionary

Use the Picture dictionary on pages 60 and 61 to practise and revise vocabulary. Invite the children to imagine what the characters in the picture are thinking or saying and to create speech bubbles to attach to the illustration. Encourage them to use the speech bubbles as a starting point for creating mini role-plays to perform in class.

Spanish culture

Create a Spanish corner (*un espacio español*) on a table or low shelf to display books about Spain and Spanish-speaking countries and souvenirs such as postcards, restaurant menus, castanets, fans and photographs. Use authentic objects or picture books to talk about Spanish history and culture whenever possible: for example, for page 53, show the children pictures of Miró's work from an art book, bring in a copy of *Don Quijote* or show a copy of Picasso's *Don Quixote* painting. Display a map of Spain to help the children to become familiar with the shape of Spain. Tell them that Spain looks a bit like a bull's head with the horns at the top.

Notes on the activities

Page 52 Yo vivo en Madrid Show the children a map of Spain. Prompt discussion about the country's geography by asking *¿Dónde está Madrid?* (Where is Madrid?) or *¿Cuál ciudad está en el sur?* (Which city is in the south?) Point to the Mediterranean Sea (to the east of Spain) and to the Pyrenees (in the northeast) and ask *¿Dónde está el Mar Mediterráneo?*, *¿Dónde están las montañas?* Prompt the children to answer using the expression *Está en el este.../Están en el norte/noreste*, etc. Once they have completed the sheet, encourage them to read their answers to the extension activity aloud. As a further extension ask *¿Dónde vive Belén?* to practise the sentences in the third person.

Page 53 ¿Cuánto sabes? Invite the children to talk about Spain. Ask what they know about its history, geography, literature, art and traditions. Create trivia cards with general knowledge questions about Spain: for example, *¿Qué es la capital de España?*, *¿Cómo se llama una aerolínea española?*, *¿Dónde está el Museo del Prado?*, etc. As an extension, invite the children to look for more images and information about the topic on each trivia card (see Oxfam's Cool Planet website which has English- and Spanish-language pages: http://www.oxfam.org.uk/coolplanet/ontheline/explore/journey/spain/geography.htm).

Page 54 Más de 1.000 Revise numbers up to 1,000 by quizzing the children with maths calculations. Invite them to write number problems on a piece of paper and then to take turns calling them out for their classmates to solve. Call out numbers over 1,000 from the word bank and ask volunteers to write them on the board in numbers and then in words. Point out that in large numbers where English places a comma, a full point is used in Spanish: for example, 2,032 (English) = 2.302 (Spanish). Conversely, the English decimal point is expressed by a comma in Spanish: 1.25 (English) = 1,25 (Spanish). The children can look up the answer to the extension activity question in a world atlas or at http://www.census.gov/main/www/popclock.html.

Page 55 El mapa del mundo Give the children a few minutes to look at the map individually and to prepare their answers before dividing them into pairs. As a follow-up activity, ask them to mark the route from their nearest city to a desired destination and to draw and label or say what type of transport they would use. Provide the children with other distances and populations to add to the map (see www.worldatlas.com for country population figures and http://www.geobytes.com/CityDistanceTool.htm to find distances between cities).

Page 56 ¿De dónde eres? Use a map of Europe to introduce the names of European countries. Revise questions such as *¿Dónde está Francia?* and prompt the children to say where it is located in relation to another country using the points of the compass. As a further extension, ask them to create a nationalities word bank showing both the masculine and feminine forms of the adjectives.

Page 57 Asociaciones Use images of people from around the world taken from magazines or books to present adjectives of nationality. Emphasise the masculine and feminine forms by saying complete sentences such as *Éste es un hombre ruso. Ésta es una mujer rusa* (This is a Russian man. This is a Russian woman). Encourage the children to repeat the sentences. Ask them to list the corresponding country for each nationality in the word bank. Invite them to suggest associations for other countries: for example, *el vino francés* (French wine).

Page 58 Sopa de letras mundial Revise the names of countries and nationalities using images of flags from books or posters. Go through the words in the list and prompt the children to identify the five continents, five countries and five nationality adjectives. For more practice, play the following geography game for which each child will need a map of the world. The children compete to be the first to guess the name of a country from oral clues such as: *El país que está al oeste de España* or *La capital de este país es Berlín*. Teach them the popular saying *'Todo el mundo es país'* ('It's a small world') and discuss what it means.

Page 59 El pasaporte Use the Picture dictionary on pages 60 and 61 to talk about what needs to be prepared for a trip and make a list. Talk about what a passport is and what sort of information it contains. Suggest that the children complete the passport with fake foreign names, nationalities and addresses. For extra practice ask the children to interview each other in role using the questions on the activity sheet. Follow up by asking individual children *¿A dónde vas?*, *¿Qué llevas en tu maleta?* and finally bidding them *¡Buen viaje!* Divide the class into small groups and ask them to organise a trip. Invite them to write down where they are going, when, what means of transport they will use, what they are taking with them, etc. Each group should then present their travel plans to the class. At the end of the course make a *Pasaporte de español* for the children with different stamps to show which topics they have covered and how much they have learned. Include a space for the child to write his or her name and other personal information. This 'passport' can be given as a diploma and shows that they can 'travel' on to the next level.

Yo vivo en Madrid

👁 **Mira el mapa.**

✏ **Completa las frases.**

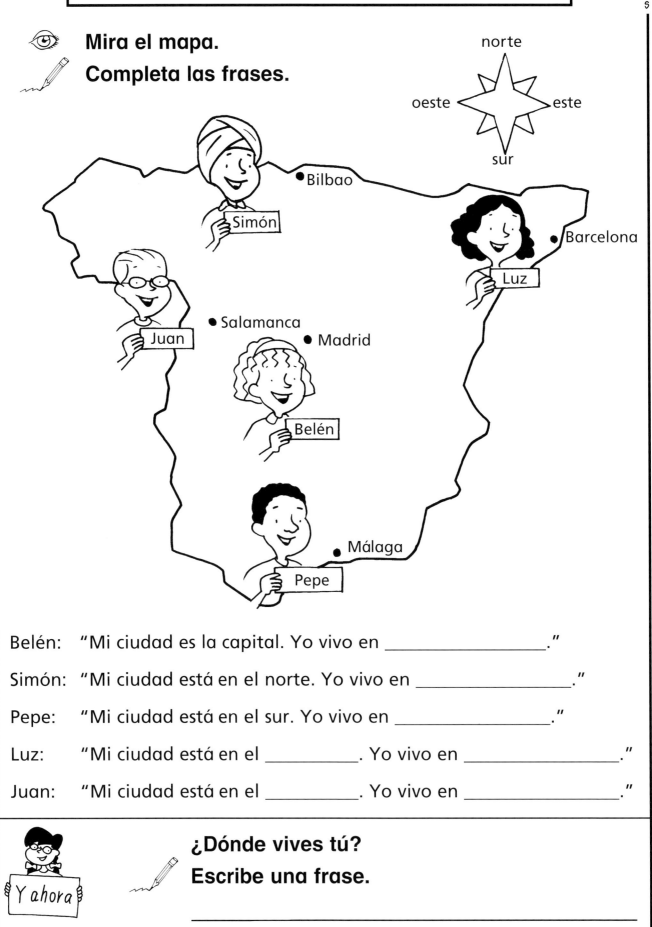

norte

oeste — este

sur

Belén: "Mi ciudad es la capital. Yo vivo en _____."

Simón: "Mi ciudad está en el norte. Yo vivo en _____."

Pepe: "Mi ciudad está en el sur. Yo vivo en _____."

Luz: "Mi ciudad está en el _____. Yo vivo en _____."

Juan: "Mi ciudad está en el _____. Yo vivo en _____."

Y ahora

¿Dónde vives tú?

✏ **Escribe una frase.**

_____

Translation: *I live in Madrid. Look at the map. Complete the sentences.* • *Where do you live? Write a sentence.*

Teachers' note: This activity familiarises the children with the map of Spain and the names of some of its cities. It also introduces compass directions and how to express where one lives. The children should answer the question in the extension activity following the model in the activity.

Developing Spanish
Libro Tres
© A & C BLACK

¿Cuánto sabes?

 Mira la lista.

Completa las frases.

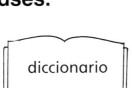 diccionario

Lista
Miguel de Cervantes
artista   los Pirineos
1492   toro
paella

---

① **Geografía**

P: ¿Cómo se llaman las montañas en el norte de España?

R: Se llaman _____.

---

② **Historia**

P: ¿En qué año descubrió América Cristóbal Colón?

R: En _____.

---

③ **Literatura**

P: ¿Quién es al autor de *Don Quijote de la Mancha*?

R: Es _____.

---

④ **Arte**

P: ¿Quién es Joan Miró?

R: Es un _____ español.

---

⑤ **Tradición**

P: ¿Qué animal se ve en una corrida?

R: Un _____.

---

⑥ **Comida**

P: ¿Cómo se llama un plato tradicional hecho con arroz?

R: Se llama _____.

 Y ahora   🔍 **Busca la respuesta.**

Tradición

P: ¿Cómo se llama un baile tradicional de España?

R: Se llama

_____.

Translation: *How much do you know? Look at the list. Complete the sentences. • Find the answer.*
Teachers' note: This activity gives some key information about Spanish culture. *P* on each card stands for *Pregunta* (question); *R* for *Respuesta* (answer). The children should refer to the word bank, the topic and the picture clue on each card to guess the answer. If necessary, they could search the Internet for the answer to the extension activity question.

Developing Spanish
Libro Tres
© A & C BLACK

Más de 1.000

Mira la lista.
Escribe los números en palabras.

diccionario

Lista

1.000	mil	100.000	cien mil
1.001	mil uno	150.000	ciento cincuenta mil
1.100	mil cien	500.000	quinientos mil
2.000	dos mil	1.000.000	un millón
10.000	diez mil	2.000.000	dos millones
10.200	diez mil doscientos	1.000.000.000	un billón

En mi aldea hay 1.800 habitantes.

__mil ochocientos__

En mi pueblo hay 3.350 habitantes.

_____

En la ciudad de Toledo hay 66.000 habitantes.

_____

En el país de España hay 40.300.000 habitantes.

_____

En el continente de Europa hay 727.000.000 de habitantes.

_____

¿Cuántos habitantes hay en el mundo?
Completa la frase.

Hay _____ de habitantes.

Translation: *Over 1,000. Look at the list. Write the numbers in words. • How many inhabitants are there in the world? Complete the sentence.*

Teachers' note: In this activity the children learn numbers above 1,000. Encourage them to pay special attention to the spellings. Point out that *millones*, the plural of *millón*, and *billones*, the plural of *billón*, have no accent. Ask the children to research the extension activity for homework.

Developing Spanish
Libro Tres
© A & C BLACK

El mapa del mundo

 Mira el mapa.

 Pregunta a tu compañero/a.

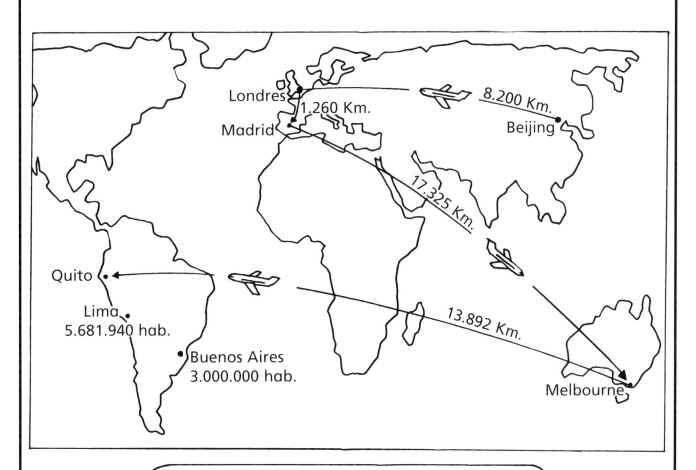

Londres
1.260 Km.
Madrid
8.200 Km.
Beijing
17.325 Km.
13.892 Km.
Quito
Lima
5.681.940 hab.
Buenos Aires
3.000.000 hab.
Melbourne

¿Cuántos Km. hay de Londres a Madrid?

Hay 1.260 Km. de Londres a Madrid.

① ¿Cuántos Km. hay de Madrid a Melbourne?

② ¿Cuántos Km. hay de Melbourne a Quito?

③ ¿Cuántos habitantes hay en Buenos Aires?

Escribe otra pregunta sobre el mapa.

Pregunta a tu compañero/a.

Translation: *Map of the world. Look at the map. Question your partner.* • *Write another question about the map. Ask your partner.*

Teachers' note: This activity practises using numbers over 1,000. Explain that *Km.* is the abbreviation for *kilómetros* (kilometres) and *hab.* is the abbreviation for *habitantes* (inhabitants). In the extension activity the children could ask about the distance from Beijing to London or about the number of inhabitants of Lima.

Developing Spanish
Libro Tres
© A & C BLACK

¿De dónde eres?

Developing Spanish
Libro Tres
© A & C BLACK

Translation: *Where are you from? Look at the list. Complete the sentences.* • *Where are you from? Write.*
Teachers' note: In this activity the children learn some European countries and nationalities. They should look at the flag and read the speaker's nationality as clues to each missing country. Ask the children to model their response in the extension activity on the speech bubbles above. Remind them to use the appropriate masculine or feminine form of the adjective of nationality.

Asociaciones

 Mira la lista.

Completa las frases.

un dragón _____

una pirámide _____

un papagayo _____

una bailarina _____

un reloj _____

una estatua _____

 **Escribe el país.**  diccionario

española ⟶ _____

griego ⟶ _____

tailandesa ⟶ _____

estadounidense ⟶ _____

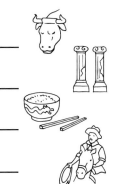

Translation: *Associations. Look at the list. Complete the sentences. • Write the country.*
Teachers' note: This activity practises gender agreement using nationality adjectives. The children should look at the picture clue and associate it with the correct adjective in the word bank. Point out that nationality adjectives are not capitalised in Spanish.

**Developing Spanish
Libro Tres
© A & C BLACK**

Sopa de letras mundial

 Mira la lista.

 Busca las palabras.

Lista

África	Europa
América	francés
Asia	griego
brasileña	Méjico
China	Oceanía
Egipto	Portugal
escocés	rusa
España	

P	O	R	T	U	G	A	L	M	E
B	A	M	É	R	I	C	A	E	U
R	E	S	P	A	Ñ	A	U	S	R
A	G	M	É	J	I	C	O	C	O
S	I	C	H	I	N	A	N	O	P
I	P	D	O	Á	F	R	I	C	A
L	T	A	F	R	A	N	C	É	S
E	O	S	B	U	P	R	U	S	A
Ñ	A	I	Í	G	R	I	E	G	O
A	S	A	O	C	E	A	N	Í	A

✏ **Divide las palabras en tres categorías:**

continentes   países   nacionalidades

Translation: *World wordsearch. Look at the list. Find the words.* • *Divide the words into three categories: continents, countries, nationalities.*

Teachers' note: This activity revises the words for some countries and nationalities and introduces the names of the five continents. Use the extension activity to assess the children's understanding of the differences between the Spanish for continents, countries and nationalities.

Developing Spanish Libro Tres © A & C BLACK

El pasaporte

 Completa el pasaporte para una persona inventada.

PASAPORTE

Nombre: _____

Apellido: _____

Fecha de nacimiento: _____

Nacionalidad: _____

Dirección: _____

_____

_____

_____

Firma: _____

 Contesta las preguntas.

¿Cómo te llamas? _____.

¿De dónde eres? _____.

¿Cómo eres? _____.

¿De qué color son tus ojos? _____.

¿Cuándo es tu cumpleaños? _____.

 Ordena las letras.

¡ n u b e   i a e v j !

_____

Translation: *Passport. Complete the passport for an imaginary person. Answer the questions. • Put the letters in order.*
Teachers' note: This activity revises how to give personal information. Tell the children to invent a character, draw him or her in the box and then use the passport details to answer the questions in complete sentences. The phrase in the extension activity is used when someone is leaving on a trip.

Developing Spanish
Libro Tres
© A & C BLACK

Picture dictionary

el pasajero

el avión

el mundo

el equipaje

la guía

Aerolíneas Españolas

la azafata

el turista

la maleta

el billete

el pasaporte

el sombrero

¡Buen viaje!

ESPAÑA

1

español/a

pesado/a

volar

reciclar

viajar

las
sandalias

las gafas
de sol

los
prismáticos

la etiqueta

la torre
de control

el piloto

Recommended resources

Teaching materials

Primary Spanish Starter Pack 1: 'Tú y yo' and Continuation Pack 2: 'Mi ciudad y mi colegio' by Ilsa Rowe and Ian Killbery, published by Early Start Languages – Primary Modern Languages Diversification Project, 7 Clanwilliam Road, Deal, Kent CT14 7BX, www.earlystart.co.uk. Resource pack with DVD/video and guide for non-specialist teachers.

Workbooks

Spanish for Beginners Pack by Angela Wilkes and John Shackell, published by Usborne, 2004. Pack contains book, workbook, sticker dictionary, flashcards, audio tape and Internet links.

Dictionaries

Spanish Dictionary for Beginners by Helen Davies and John Shackell, published by Usborne, 2002.

DK First Spanish Picture Dictionary published by Dorling Kindersley, 2005.

Oxford Spanish Dictionary: Spanish–English, English–Spanish by Beatriz Galimberti Jarman, Roy Russell, Carol Styles Carvajal, Jane Horwood, published by Oxford University Press, 2003.

Websites for teachers

www.bbc.co.uk/languages/spanish
Hear Spanish spoken and test your Spanish using simple games, vocabulary and grammar exercises. There is a specific link for primary school Spanish teachers and children.

www.cnice.mecd.es/ninos
Links directory compiled by the Spanish Ministry of Education and Science. In Spanish.

www.cvc.cervantes.es
Material for Spanish-language teachers and students. Up-to-date information about cultural events. Offers an interactive page for children. In Spanish.

www.guiainfantil.com
Spanish website for parents, teachers and carers. A good resource for cultural information, songs, stories, etc.

www.ihmadrid.com/comunicativo
Spanish-language resources, activities, lesson plans, self-correcting grammar exercises.

www.sgci.mec.es/uk
Spanish Embassy site with details about Spanish education and culture. Links to *Tecla*, an online magazine for Spanish-language teachers and learners.

Websites for children

www.bbc.co.uk/schools/primaryspanish/index.shtml
Fun online Spanish-language activities for children. There is also a section with tips for Spanish teachers.

www.milcuentos.com
Spanish website with children's stories, including audio.

www.pdictionary.com
Multilingual Internet picture dictionary.

Curriculum information and teaching methods

The Department of Education and Skills
Modern Foreign Language Team
Sanctuary Buildings, Area 4D
London SW1P 3BT
tel: 020 7925 6291
e-mail: MFL.team@dfes.gsi.gov.uk
website: www.dfes.gov.uk/languages

The National Centre for Languages (CILT)
20 Bedfordbury
London WC2N 4LB
tel: 020 7379 5101
e-mail: info@cilt.org.uk
website: www.cilt.org.uk

The National Advisory Centre on Early Language Learning (NACELL)
20 Bedfordbury
London WC2N 4LB
tel: 020 7379 5101 Ext. 286
e-mail: nacell@cilt.org.uk
website: www.nacell.org.uk

The Qualifications and Curriculum Authority (QCA)
83 Piccadilly
London W1J 8QA
tel: 020 7509 5555
e-mail: info@qca.org.uk
website: www.qca.org.uk

Suppliers of books and teaching materials

Bilingual Supplies for Children
PO Box 4081
Bournemouth
Dorset BH8 9ZZ
website: www.bilingual-supplies.co.uk

Early Start Languages
74 Middle Deal Road
Kent CT14 9RH
tel: 01304 362 569
e-mail: orders@earlystart.co.uk
website: www.earlystart.co.uk

European Schoolbooks Limited
The Runnings
Cheltenham
Gloucestershire GL51 9PQ
tel: 01242 245252
e-mail: direct@esb.co.uk
website: www.eurobooks.co.uk

The European Bookshop
5 Warwick Street
London W1B 5LU
tel: 020 7734 5259
e-mail: mrg@esb.co.uk

Answers

p11
1 *lunes*
2 *martes*
3 *miércoles*
4 *jueves*
5 *viernes*
6 *sábado*
7 *domingo*

Y ahora
domingo   *lunes*   *martes*
miércoles   *jueves*   *viernes*
sábado   *domingo*   *lunes*

p12
Clockwise, starting from *enero*:
febrero   *agosto*
marzo   *septiembre*
abril   *octubre*
mayo   *noviembre*
junio   *diciembre*
julio

p13
1 *Es el primero de enero.*
2 *Es el cinco de marzo.*
3 *Es el catorce de abril.*
4 *Es el veinticinco de junio.*
5 *Es el once de julio.*
6 *Es el trece de septiembre.*
7 *Es el veinte de octubre.*
8 *Es el primero de diciembre.*

p14
1 *Mi cumpleaños es el veinte de marzo.*
2 *Mi cumpleaños es el trece de septiembre.*
3 *Mi cumpleaños es el dieciocho de enero.*
4 *Mi cumpleaños es el once de agosto.*
5 *Mi cumpleaños es el primero de julio.*
6 *Mi cumpleaños es el veintiocho de febrero.*

p15
1 *Pilar*
2 *Pamplona*
3 *emocionante*
4 *corren*
5 *miedo*

p17
1 *Es la una y cinco.*
2 *Son las dos y veinte.*
3 *Son las tres y veinticinco.*
4 *Son las siete menos veinticinco.*
5 *Es la una menos diez.*

p18
La fiesta es el veinte de mayo.
La fiesta es a las cuatro.
La fiesta es el quince de junio.
La fiesta es a las cinco y media.

p22
       nieva
hace viento   *hace calor*
hace sol   *hace frío*   *llueve*

Y ahora
¿Qué tiempo hace?

p23
Y ahora
En Madrid hace sol.

p24
primavera   *verano*
otoño   *invierno*
falso   *verdadero*
verdadero   *verdadero*

p25
Carlos:
el abrigo
las botas
la bufanda
los guantes
el jersey

Marta:
la camiseta
las gafas de sol
los pantalones cortos
las sandalias
el traje de baño

p26
En primavera hace fresco. Llevo un jersey.
En verano hace sol. Llevo unas gafas de sol.
En otoño llueve. Llevo un impermeable.
En invierno hace frío. Llevo una bufanda.

Cuando llueve llevo un paraguas.
Cuando hace frío llevo un abrigo.
Cuando hace calor llevo pantalones cortos.
Cuando nieva llevo botas.

p27

P	A	R	A	G	U	A	S	M	S
R	A	L	L	U	E	V	E	A	I
I	J	C	V	A	R		T	Y	N
M	E	A	I	N	A	O	V	B	V
A	R	L	E	T	B	F	E	U	I
V	S	O	N	E	R	R	R	F	E
E	E	R	T	S	I	Í	A	A	R
R	Y	S	O		G	O	N	N	N
A	O	L	O	T	O	Ñ	O	D	O
	S	A	N	D	A	L	I	A	S

Y ahora
MAR Y SOL

p34
1 *Yo me levanto a las seis y media.*
2 *¿A qué hora vas a la escuela?*
    Yo voy a la escuela a las ocho menos cuarto.

3 ¿A qué hora haces los deberes?
Yo hago los deberes a las cinco menos diez.
4 ¿A qué hora te acuestas?
Yo me acuesto a las nueve y media.

p36
Son las siete y cuarto. José desayuna.
Son las tres. Pilar regresa a casa.
Son las cinco menos veinte. Felipe hace monopatín.
Son las nueve y diez. Carla ve la tele.
Son las diez y media. Julio duerme.
Y ahora
A las ocho y cinco Tomás corre.

p42
¿Diga?
¿Está Marta, por favor?
¿Está José, por favor? No, no está.
¿Está María, por favor? Sí. Un momento, ahora
                          se pone.
¿Está el Sr. Ruiz, por favor? No, se ha equivocado.

p43
	los dibujos animados	el concurso
el documental	la película	la telenovela
el telediario	el control remoto	la parabólica

p45
Y ahora
el disquete   el disco compacto

p46
1 falso   **2** falso
3 verdadero   **4** verdadero
Y ahora
1 Carlos invita a Paco a su casa a las tres de la tarde.
2 Carlos tiene que estudiar historia.

p47
Papel: el folleto, la revista, el periódico, el catálogo
Plástico: la botella de champú, la botella de
   detergente, la botella de agua
Vidrio: la botella de vino, el frasco, el tarro

p49
Across: Down:
2 control remoto   **1** contenedor
7 basura   **3** televisor
8 pantalla   **4** ratón
9 impresora   **5** ordenador
                       6 papelera

Y ahora
reciclar

p52
Yo vivo en Madrid.
Yo vivo en Bilbao.
Yo vivo en Málaga.
Mi ciudad está en el este. Yo vivo en Barcelona.
Mi ciudad está en el oeste. Yo vivo en Salamanca.

p53
1 los Pirineos   **2** 1492
3 Miguel de Cervantes **4** artista
5 toro   **6** paella
Y ahora
flamenco

p54
tres mil trescientos cincuenta
sesenta y seis mil
cuarenta millones trescientos mil
setecientos veintisiete millones
Y ahora
6.500.000.000 (or 6,5 billones)

p55
1 Hay 17.325 Km. de Madrid a Melbourne.
2 Hay 13.892 Km. de Melbourne a Quito.
3 Hay 3.000.000 de habitantes en Buenos Aires.
Y ahora
¿Cuántos Km. hay de Beijing a Londres?
Hay 8.200 Km. de Beijing a Londres.
¿Cuántos habitantes hay en Lima?
Hay 5.681.940 habitantes en Lima.

p56
	Gales
Inglaterra	Francia
Alemania	Portugal
Irlanda	Escocia

p57
Un dragón chino.   Una pirámide egipcia.
Un papagayo brasileño. Una bailarina rusa.
Un reloj suizo.   Una estatua india.
Y ahora
España   Tailandia
Grecia   Estados Unidos

p58

P	O	R	T	U	G	A	L	M	E
B	A	M	É	R	I	C	A	E	U
R	E	S	P	A	Ñ	A	U	S	R
A	G	M	É	J	I	C	O	C	O
S	I	C	H	I	N	A	N	O	P
I	P	D	O	Á	F	R	I	C	A
L	T	A	F	R	A	N	C	É	S
E	O	S	B	U	P	R	U	S	A
Ñ	A	I	Í	G	R	I	E	G	O
A	S	A	O	C	E	A	N	Í	A

Y ahora
Continentes: África, América, Asia, Europa, Oceanía
Países: China, Egipto, España, Méjico, Portugal
Nacionalidades: brasileña, escocés, francés, griego, rusa

p59
Y ahora
¡Buen viaje!